Weaving High Performance Multiprocessor Fabric

Architectural insights into the Intel® QuickPath Interconnect

Robert A. Maddox
Gurbir Singh
Robert J. Safranek

Intel
PRESS

ISBN 13: 978-1-934053-18-8

This book is printed on acid-free paper. ∞

Publisher: Richard Bowles
Managing Editor: Bruce Bartlett
Editor: David J. Clark
Text Design & Composition: STI Certified
Graphic Art: STI Certified (illustrations), Ron Bohart (cover)

Library of Congress Cataloging in Publication Data:

Printed in China

10 9 8 7 6 5 4 3 2 1

First printing, Version 1.0 July 2009

IMPORTANT

You can access the companion Web site for this book on the Internet at:

www.intel.com/intelpress/qpi

Use the serial number located in the upper-right hand corner of the last page to register your book and access additional material, including the Digital Edition of the book.

It has been my great privilege to have been involved with so many highly talented people, both inside Intel Corporation and among our customers, as we took the journey to bring this technology to life. In particular I would like to dedicate this book to the outstanding group of Intel TMEs and FAEs involved in the enabling of the first Intel QPI products, and to the many internal and external students that I have had the opportunity to help coach and tutor a bit along the way.

On a personal note I would like to dedicate this book to my wife Dale for her support throughout. Finally, to the future generation represented by our children and their families: Robert, Courtney, and Jackson Maddox, Rebecca and Joey Smith. My hope is that in some way these efforts have contributed and will contribute positively to their future.

—R. A. M.

I dedicate this book to the members of the architecture team who were responsible for the definition of this interface. Their creativity, enthusiasm, and dogged determination to do the right thing made this a truly memorable project, one that I am really proud to be a part of. Thanks.

I would also like to dedicate this book to my uncle Mr. Amrik Singh, who was my true mentor and idol. He, an engineer himself, showed me the joys and challenges of creating things and taught me valuable lessons they never could or did teach in any school.

—G. S.

I have been involved with the development of this specification from the beginning. I was very fortunate to have worked with a vast group of highly motivated individuals from many projects across of Intel Corporation. I was given the honor to represent an incredible development team in the Nehalem program. So for all involved in the Nehalem Uncore, this book is for you.

I especially would like to dedicate this book to my departed father; who drilled into my head "things that are designed right the first time work the first time." I guess he always knew that I was destined to be an engineer.

—R.J.S.

Contents

Contents

Chapter 2   Intel® QuickPath Interconnect in Operation   35

Chapter 3   **Linking Two Devices   81**

Chapter 5   **Advanced System Considerations   189**

Foreword

Here is what many of us CPU designers are secretly thinking: what's up with I/O design? How hard can it be to shovel bits from one place to another? The answer is: Not hard at all if

a) you don't care about performance and

b) if you don't care about correctness.

Any fool can get wrong answers, and moderately talented ones can do it at arbitrarily fast bitrates.

But if you're so picky that not just any bits will do, you want the right bits and you want them Right Now, then you're just the kind of person that these authors had in mind. And next you'll be wanting power management modes, error detection and correction, hot plug capability, and whipped cream on your mint hot chocolate. Well, these authors can help you with those too, if you spot them the mint hot chocolate and the whipped cream.

Another thing CPU designers know, even if they'd rather eat dirt than admit it (and they'll probably kick me out of the CPU architects' club and change the secret handshake for my revealing this): for all their struggles to produce fast processing systems, the rate at which their voracious engines can produce useful answers is often governed by the I/O design, not by the chest-thumping wizardry with which they've imbued the processor cores.

If the CPU is the brain of the system, then I/O is the combined blood supply and nervous system. If the brain is slow, then maybe you lurch around some but you'll still get there. But if the blood supply or nervous system is not cutting it, you don't move at all, game over. And you'll drop your mint hot chocolate all over the keyboard, thus voiding the warranty.

All this could be avoided with Intel® QuickPath Interconnect (Intel® QPI) features like lane reversal, polarity reversal, clock failover, and self-healing links. No, lane reversal is not related to driving while texting on your cell phone, and polarity reversal has nothing to do with spousal mood swings. Those are probably your own fault, and clock failover isn't going to help you there. The self-healing links might, though. You have to read the book to be sure. But you should do that in any case.

The Intel QPI is not your father's bus. (Unless you're one of Gurbir's kids.) There is a great deal of complexity to this interconnect structure, but it's okay, it's a complexity borne of a lot of good ideas, intelligently interwoven and logically explained. The Intel QPI makes sense, especially with these three authors as your personal tutors. For example, the physical links in an Intel QPI fabric configure themselves as they go for highest data integrity and speed, and if one of them breaks, the failure is automatically handled, reported, and routed around. Would that drivers on a highway could do as well. The how's, why's and wherefores are all covered here.

Authors Safranek and Maddox have long distinguished careers in interconnect design, validation, architecture, and computer system design. Gurbir Singh has been designing buses since the electron was invented, and it shows. Go back and check those cans-connected-by-a-string you played with as a kid. See what it says in fine print on the cans? Yep. That was Gurbir too.

The cool thing about this book is of course the interconnect technology. What's fun is that the authors have managed to describe the Intel QPI in such an interesting way. Even for inveterate geeks like me, most technical books are dry as dust and work much better than insomnia pills. They should come with warning stickers: Do not operate heavy machinery for a week after reading this book. Not this book though: *Weaving High Performance Multiprocessor Fabric* is engaging, educational, well-organized and directly useful. It doesn't get any better than that.

Robert P. Colwell

Preface

Vision is about seeing the invisible

—Jonathan Swift

Any modern microprocessor-based computing system is comprised of a collection of sophisticated high performance components. Processors, memory devices, and input/output controllers are the building blocks from which the computer is constructed. These devices are very tangible evidence of the rapid ongoing advances in silicon technology and manufacturing methods. What is less easily discerned is the underlying fabric, or system interconnect, that ties together these elements. As the demands placed upon computing systems have continued to go up, the demands upon this fabric have also increased. This is especially apparent in systems composed of multiple processors. In addition to the silicon advances predicted by Moore's Law, architectural advances are needed to allow these system to reach their full potential. As we shall see, the Intel® QuickPath Interconnect (Intel® QPI) is one of those key architectural advances.

The Front Side Bus (FSB) was introduced in 1994 with the Intel® Pentium® Pro processor to support symmetric multi-processing. Over time, this architecture evolved to meet the growing needs of platforms based on it. Seymour Cray once said performance is all about balance. The proper balance between processor capacity, memory capacity, and system bandwidth is the goal of platform architects. In a constant pursuit to enhance performance, Intel architects integrated the memory controller into the microprocessor and used a high-speed point-to-point, packetized interconnect as the processor bus. This effort has now come to fruition with the first processors employing such technology being the next generation Intel® microarchitectures code-named Nehalem and Tukwila. Along with the new internal microarchitecture comes the Intel® QuickPath Architecture, which is Intel's first major system interconnect transition since the introduction of the FSB.

A significant characteristic of the Intel QuickPath Architecture is that it facilitates multiple point-to-point connections among all the devices. There is no single bus that all the processors must use and contend with each other to reach memory and I/O. Coupled with Intel's large cache memory implementations, this architectural approach enables the performance of servers and workstations to take another leap forward.

Who Should Read This Book

Our intent has always been to present the basic principles, features, and options of the Intel QuickPath Interconnect at the conceptual level so that the reader can grasp the overall intent of the specific capability. We are assuming a certain level of understanding in computer interconnects and/ or topologies; however, it is difficult to describe the complete list of individuals who might be interested in reading this book. At a minimum the reader should possess the computer nerd gene, or else this book would be the perfect cure for insomnia. If the reader is fortunate enough to be blessed with one of the super nerd genes, then he or she should consider this book to be a good primer for the even more detailed Intel QuickPath Interconnect product specifications. If you are one of these special people, and have an innovative project in mind, you should get in touch with an Intel representative so that you might get an opportunity to delve down into the depths of those documents!

Our primary goal has been to provide an overview of the features we think are necessary in a system topology for today and the future. We could not describe all enabling features of the Intel QuickPath Interconnect given the constraints of providing this book in a timely manner (and for the most part the features are described more in breadth than in depth).

As implied earlier, it is fair to say that Intel does not provide this level of investment unless it intends to leverage a technology for years to come. Just look at the Intel QuickPath Interconnect's predecessor, the Front Side Bus. Variations of that technology were the fundamental interconnect for well over a decade for every Intel-based laptop, desktop, and server. It is envisioned that the fundamentals of the Intel QuickPath Interconnect will be a key component in all Intel-based servers for at least the next decade. For this simple reason, the contents of this book are significant to the computer industry at large and the fundamental reason it should be read.

What's in Store in This Book

This book describes how the Intel QPI meets the challenges of high performance multiprocessor system design. It is not a rehash of the architecture's specifications, nor does it attempt to be an implementation handbook. This book does provide a broad overview of the technology elements used to create this new system interconnect, and discusses how these elements interact to deliver the rich set of capabilities required for next generation systems. It gets to the "why" behind the specifications and presents the details in an approachable manner. The goal is to raise the reader's overall understanding of the Intel QuickPath Architecture, without getting into the specific requirements involved with the actual design of any device or platform that implements this new interconnect.

The book's content maintains a logical flow from high level operations, down into more specifics. For the reader interested in learning the basics, the first two chapters are recommended reading for a solid overview. The remaining four chapters are a deeper dive into the mechanisms and capabilities of the Intel QPI. Those later chapters can be examined as needed at the reader's pace for developing more in-depth knowledge.

You are invited go to this book's companion Web page at www.intel.com/intelpress/qpi for a digital edition of the book, training information and live reference links.

Chapter Content Guide

Chapter 1 discusses the evolution of various platforms, leading up to the development of the Intel QPI. After illustrating the problems of cache coherency in a multiple processor system, the chapter goes on to define the overall Intel QuickPath Architecture and goes through many of its key attributes.

Chapter 2 takes a top-down approach in describing the operational flows of several types of transactions. It provides good insight into the underlying mechanisms used to accomplish various functions such as memory, I/O, and interrupt cycles. In particular it delves into how cache coherency is managed in a multiprocessor system using the Intel QPI.

Chapter 3 presents the details of how two devices establish a connection between themselves. This goes into the inner workings of the physical and link layers that together form the foundation of the new interconnect. It describes the logical, electrical, and virtual networking capabilities required to support the messages being sent and received by the upper layers of the architecture. For those readers interested in more specifics regarding the electrical aspects of Intel QPI, please refer to the companion book *Mastering High Performance Multiprocessor Signaling: Electrical design with the Intel® QuickPath Interconnect*, by Dave Coleman and Michael Mirmak.

Chapter 4 discusses the process by which the system initializes itself in preparation for running an operating system. It pays particular attention to the functions that are new and unique to platforms based on the Intel QPI, including new responsibilities of the system boot firmware.

Chapter 5 covers many of the advanced high level system functions that are part of the overall set of capabilities anticipated for this new platform architecture. This includes several forms of Dynamic Reconfiguration, the ability to add, remove, or reconfigure various system resources without taking down the platform. Power and fault management topics are also included in this section.

Chapter 6 covers the capabilities put into the system architecture that enable the detection of, and recovery from, the occurrence of various types of hard or soft failures in parts of the system. These reliability, availability, and serviceability (or RAS) functions are a vital aspect of creating and validating robust systems based on the Intel QPI.

Note

> The contents of this book are intended only as an overall guide to understanding the basics of the Intel® QuickPath Architecture. Parties interested in creating either system or component level designs utilizing this technology should contact their local Intel representative for additional information.
>
> The overall Intel® QuickPath Architecture allows for a great deal of implementation flexibility and modular future growth, all within the scope of the architecture. In later sections of this text when we talk of certain characteristics of Intel QPI, we are generally referring to current implementations. Those examples should not be construed as future limitations on the overall scope of the Intel® QuickPath Architecture.

Authors' Background

Robert A. Maddox completed his Master of Science in Electrical Engineering degree from Georgia Tech, then went to work on a variety of small scale computing projects with NCR Corporation, and worked on several aspects of design, validation, and production of medium scale server systems. This included work with both the Front-Side Bus and I/O buses used in multiprocessor servers. Robert joined Intel Corporation in 1998 and moved into working on the pre-silicon validation aspects of a server I/O hub. His latest assignment as a staff technical marketing engineer in the Server Platforms Group has him focused on the emerging Intel QuickPath Interconnect, working both with internal teams and external companies involved in the application of this new platform interconnect. On the life side of the work/life equation, Robert enjoys time with his family, photography, tennis, playing in a musical group, and the occasional jog around the neighborhood.

Gurbir Singh is a senior principal engineer in the Digital Enterprise Architecture and Planning Group at Intel. Gurbir led the architecture team defining the Intel QuickPath Interconnect. Gurbir has 31 years of experience in CPU and platform architecture. He joined Intel Corporation in 1984 and has worked on the architecture of several CPUs including the Intel® Pentium® Pro processor and its successors: the Intel Pentium II, Pentium III, and Pentium 4 processors. He was responsible for the architecture of the caches and system interfaces (the Front Side Bus) for many Intel processors. Most recently he worked on the Intel® Core™ i7 project that introduces the Intel QuickPath Interconnect. He holds thirty patents in the field of system interfaces and cache architecture. He received his Master of Science degree from Clemson University and Bachelor of Science degree from the Indian Institute of Technology, Kharagpur. When Gurbir is not working on multiprocessor system interfaces he enjoys amateur astronomy and tinkering in his machine shop.

Robert J. Safranek is a principal engineer in the Digital Enterprise Architecture and Planning Group at Intel. He attained his bachelor's degree from the University of Nebraska and master's degree from Portland State University. For ten years he developed products in the area of communications, telecommunications, and high performance I/O architectures for computer systems. For the last seventeen years Robert has been developing NUMA and CC-NUMA architectures, resolving cache coherency and memory consistency issues for link-based systems for Sequent and IBM. He joined Intel Corporation in 2000 and has been working on the Intel QuickPath Interconnect definition since its inception and was the primary architect for the first platforms based on the Intel QuickPath Interconnect. Outside of Intel, now with their sons grown, Robert and his wife try to spend as many days outside as possible; on slopes in the winter, golf, backpacking and other outdoor activities throughout the spring and summer.

Acknowledgements

This book would not have been possible without the numerous contributions from a large number of people inside and outside of Intel. While it will not be possible to mention all by name, we can recognize the different categories of people involved along the way.

For The Technology

First of all, hats off to the senior technical staff and management of Intel who had the foresight and skill to put in place the plans, resources, and teams required to bring this new technology to market. It would be hard to overstate the magnitude of this change, which is a fundamental and significant part of next generation Intel workstations and servers. Truly a huge bet in terms of its impact on the Corporation.

Next, we would be remiss without mentioning the highly skilled and dedicated individuals that comprise the planning, architecture, design, technical marketing, product marketing, software, validation, and manufacturing teams that worked relentlessly to make the technology concepts happen in real products, produced in high volumes. To the Nehalem, Tukwila, Beckton Tylersburg, and other related teams, a big salute. What we describe in this book is the technology that these people have lived every day.

To the various members of the Intel QPI Core Team and TXT groups, our thanks for your leadership and direction that resulted in the successful execution of these programs.

For The Book

While the names of everyone that contributed in some way to the actual Intel QuickPath Technology would be impossible to accurately capture, we would like to pay special recognition to several individuals who directly contributed to making this book happen.

Stephen S. Pawlowski, Intel Senior Fellow and CTO of the Intel Digital Enterprise Group gave us essential encouragement to create and publish this book for which we are most grateful. The support of Intel Press Publisher Richard Bowles throughout the project is very much appreciated.

We are deeply indebted for the major contributions of Intel Senior Principle Engineer Eric Delano and Intel Technical Lead Engineer Jeff Willey, who bravely stepped in and provided substantial content on the more complex detailed subjects discussed in Chapters 5 and 6.

The utmost credit goes to the various technical reviewers of the book, who have not only provided the suggestions and corrections on the text in the book, but also provided portions of the content. For that we are very grateful.

We deeply appreciate the contributions of Robert P. Colwell for his technical review and comments, and especially for his quintessential Foreword to our book.

We enjoyed working with Ravi Budruk of MindShare and are grateful for his detailed technical review and comments regarding the entire book.

We are grateful to the technical reviews from our Intel colleagues who provided technical content, review comments, and expert answers to our questions. This list includes but is not limited to: George Kunz, Scott Huck,

Klaus Roth, Leslie Xu, Gary DeLeon, Gini Volini, Ian McCollum, Venkat Iyer, Li-Gao Zei, and Michael Nesheiwat.

We are very thankful to the many contributions of the external reviewers: Houssiaux Sophie of Bull, Tom Walley of Avago Technologies, Di Mu of Super Micro Computer, Inc., Bryan Hornung of Hewlett Packard, Yoshihisa Yamada of NEC Computer Technologies, Ltd., Masahiro Tokoro of Hitachi Ltd., Keith Wilkinson and Roland Dreier of Cisco Systems, Edward Leigh and Simon Czermak of Fujitsu-Siemens, Scott Diesing of Cray, and Greg Waters of Sun Microsystems.

We would also like to extend our sincere thanks to our management, Gene Pitts, Boyd Davis, Ganapati Srinivasa, Dan Casaletto, and John Hengeveld who encouraged and directed us to spend time creating the book. We offer a special thanks to Pete MacWilliams for his constant support and gentle guidance throughout the long effort of creating and defining this interface.

Managing editor Bruce Bartlett believed in us and kept putting the project back on track after numerous resets. He kept us motivated through the gentlest but most persistent of nudges. Editor David Clark helped immensely to ensure we did not assault the English language too terribly and cleaned up after us diligently. The production team took the raw material and made a great looking book from it. We especially appreciate the work of Ron Bohart, the artist who created the intriguing cover art.

Kelly Sweeney and Kirti Devi performed a pivotal role in getting the word out about the book through their marketing efforts.

For anyone we may have missed, please accept our deepest apologies.

Robert A. Maddox

Gurbir Singh

Robert J. Safranek

April 2009

Chapter 1

A First Look at the Intel® QuickPath Interconnect

Nature uses only the longest threads to weave her patterns, so that each small piece of her fabric reveals the organization of the entire tapestry.
—Richard Feynman

One of the most far reaching inventions of the last century has been the microprocessor. This little computer built on a tiny sliver of silicon has invaded almost every aspect of industrialized society. As the technology of the microprocessor has advanced over the last four decades, so has its ability to connect to more devices in the real world, or work in concert with other microprocessors and create scalable computer systems. Let us take a look at the technology that has made this possible and study the capabilities of the most advanced version of the interconnect fabric delivered by Intel, the Intel® QuickPath Interconnect (Intel® QPI).

Evolution of Microprocessor Interconnect

The invention of the microprocessor started a revolution in computing. The Intel 4004, the first commercial single chip microprocessor, was very basic in its design and architecture with very modest instruction and data rates.

These rates matched well with the memory technology of the day, and very usable and balanced systems could be constructed by directly connecting the processor to memory. A system bus served as the interconnect mechanism and carried the data between the memory subsystem and the processor.

The microprocessor has evolved over time, driven along by improvements in microarchitecture, manyfold increases in clock rates, and advancements in silicon design and manufacturing techniques. This increase in computing power demanded greater data rates from the memory system. Corresponding improvements were made in DRAM technology and the requirements for data were readily met by the memory systems of the day. The technology of signaling also improved and the data rate of the system interface kept up with the rest of the devices.

Things changed in the 1980s with the advent of more sophisticated, pipe-lined microarchitectures, such as the Intel® 80486 processor. The DRAMs could no longer keep pace with the data rates required and cache memory was introduced into microprocessor based designs. This high speed memory is built with fast SRAM technology. It has low latency and the high data rates required to keep the processor operating without stalling while waiting for data from the relatively slower DRAMs. However, cache memory devices are generally considerably more expensive and power hungry than slower DRAMs, so cache sizes tend to be small in order to provide the greater speed at a reasonable system cost. As a result, caches store only a small portion of the data from the main system memory. They rely on the facts that typical programs are composed of small sequences of straight line code that loop back to repeatedly execute the same code many times, and that programs tend to operate on the same set of data entities for a while before moving on to the next set of data. In other words, caches take advantage of the idea of spatial and temporal locality, the idea that if you access data, you are highly likely to access nearby data.

A cache memory exploits these characteristics to provide a significant reduction in latency and to achieve high data throughput. The cache sub-system does so by fetching sequences of data from system memory beyond that which is immediately requested by the processor and storing it for fast access when needed. The system interconnect evolved to serve as the interface between the cache and the system memory and typically carries sequential bursts of data entities called *cache lines*. A cache line can be anywhere from 16 to 128 bytes of sequentially addressed data depending upon the design of the cache. The system memory, typically built with DRAM devices is well suited to provide such a burst of contiguously addressed data at high speed. The signaling technology of the interconnect also evolved to run at higher data rates, keeping up with the needs of the faster processors.

The next change in computers and interconnect systems occurred in the early 1990s with the introduction of multiprocessor systems. Two or more processors were connected to a common, shared memory system over the system interconnect. These processors operated in concert to share the overall workload and provided higher performance when compared to a single processor system. The system interconnect had to evolve yet again to efficiently handle requests from all the processors in the system. This was achieved by fairly handling requests between all the processors and efficiently pipelining their requests to memory. The signaling technology was updated to handle the electrical loads of multiple processors on a single bus at high transfer rates. The system interconnect was also enhanced to properly share the information cached in the processors.

The Intel® Pentium® Pro microprocessor was the first Intel architecture microprocessor to provide a system interconnect, the Front Side Bus (also abbreviated as the FSB), which supported symmetric multiprocessing. The FSB can connect up to four processors, a memory controller, and an I/O controller. The FSB can pipeline up to eight transactions for high throughput. The FSB also provides mechanisms to ensure that all the processors' caches share data from system memory properly and do not use stale data that has been modified in another processor's cache. Sharing data coherently between caches is a key capability required in any high performance system interconnect.

The FSB served the needs of the Intel Pentium Pro family of processors and was then enhanced to meet the needs of the Intel Pentium 4 processors that followed. Improvements in bus bandwidth were achieved by increasing the data transfer rates. A modified form of Gunning transceiver logic (called GTL+) signaling is used by some products to operate the FSB at clock rates of 400 MHz, and therefore deliver quad-pumped information transfer rates of up to 1.6 gigatransfers per second (GT/s). Part of the bandwidth improvement was made possible by reducing the number of processors connected to a single bus down to two (dual independent bus) and eventually to one (dedicated high speed bus). Reducing the number of devices connected to a FSB mitigates some board routing and signal quality concerns and therefore removes some obstacles of getting to higher data rates. Thus a four processor system required four FSBs to connect the four processors to a single central memory controller. This proved to be an expensive solution in that the memory controller hub (MCH), the chipset providing the memory and I/O interfaces on the platform, required over a thousand pins just to accommodate the four FSBs. More MCH pins were needed to handle the interface to memory. Moreover a single memory controller may become a bottleneck in the system that limits both the memory size and bandwidth that could be built into a system.

The architects of the Intel QuickPath Interconnect started by taking a fresh look at the needs of the entire system, striving to provide a complete solution that addressed future growth requirements. Intel QPI is intended to provide a very capable system interconnect fabric that is at the heart of scalable, high performance systems. Of course, due to its usage in very high production volumes, Intel QPI had to provide these functions while also keeping system and silicon costs as low as possible. The Intel QuickPath Architecture has been designed for future generations of Intel processors and provides plenty of headroom for growth in performance and features. Intel QPI achieves these goals through the use of narrow, packetized, cache-coherent, message based, high speed point-to-point links that use less than half the number of signals of the FSB. This results in lower package and routing costs and yet provides over fifty percent more bandwidth for higher performance. Intel QPI is also very flexible, allowing one to build highly scalable systems around multiple processors, memory controllers, and I/O controllers. Systems can choose to integrate the memory controller and I/O controllers onto the same die with the processor. Such systems can be upgraded in a modular fashion. Every processor added to a system will bring additional memory bandwidth and capacity with its integrated memory controller, and provide a very cost effective upgrade that offers a well balanced system. The Intel QPI cache coherence protocol also provides an efficient means to resolve cache coherence issues involving multiple processors.

Let us look at the issues created by multiple caches in a system and ways to keep them coherent so that all processors will always get the most up-to-date information. We will then describe the high performance cache coherence mechanisms in Intel QPI, and how these mechanisms can handle systems containing a large number of devices such as processors and intelligent I/O controllers.

Solving the Cache Coherency Problem

Whenever multiple processors, each with its own cache, cooperate to access and modify data in a shared memory system, they run the risk of accessing stale or outdated data that may have been modified by one of the other processors. This cache coherency problem can be best illustrated by an example from the real world.

Let us say that Mary, an attorney in a law firm, has to draw up a legal contract. She pulls together a team of experts, Robert, Janice, Patty, and Tom, who will all help to create the final document. Mary starts with a boilerplate form of the contract and creates a table of contents assigning page numbers to each section. She shares this with her team. She then prints out the boilerplate document and places it in a central location accessible to the entire team.

Robert decides he needs to study pages seven through ten and makes copies of those pages and takes them to his office for his own use. Similarly, Janice decides she needs pages eight through ten and copies and takes them. Similarly Patty and Tom make copies of pages that are of interest to them and the end result is that all four team members now have copies of document pages in their own respective offices (caches). Multiple copies of any page can exist locally, and each individual can refer to his or her own copy.

If Robert decides that he has no further use for page nine he can destroy his copy of that page. This ability to cache copies of pages works well as long as no member makes any changes to the pages in his or her office. However if Robert decides to change the contents of page ten then he must take steps to ensure that Janice is not working with obsolete information on her copy of that page. If Janice also decides to update page ten, she makes the problem even worse. This is the basis of the problem of cache coherency.

The team must institute a set of rules on how to handle updates in order to ensure that they have a graceful way of collaborating to produce an accurate document containing all the latest changes. This set of rules can range from something very simple but restrictive and with much overhead, to one that is more sophisticated and lets each team member work much more autonomously. Let us look at two ways of keeping the caches coherent.

Write-Through Caching

The team can follow a simple set of rules whenever anyone decides to update a page. In our example above when Robert is ready to update page ten he tells the other team members that he is doing so, giving them the page number. They all check to see if they have copies of the pages and if so, every team member except Robert will destroy their copies. Robert then makes the change to page ten and places it at the central location. Robert can choose to keep a copy for himself, if he desires. If Janice now decides to make a change to the same page, she must go to the central location for the latest copy as she destroyed her copy of the page when Robert announced his intention to update page ten. She too must announce to all that she is about to change page ten and they all, including Robert, must destroy their copies of that page. Once she makes her update, she must then place a copy of the updated page ten in the central location. In case both Robert and Janice decided to make the change simultaneously they can toss a coin to decide who goes first. The other team member will then have to fetch the updated copy from the central location to merge in his or her updates. This mechanism, in computer architecture referred to as *write-through caching,* is the simplest form of a cache coherence mechanism for handling updates. A simple and efficient mechanism is required to announce which page is being changed. Each team member must always take the time to put the most up-to-date copy of the page in the central location after every update, for all the others to use.

Write-Back Caching

The team members decide that writing through to the central location is unnecessary overhead. Each team member should be able to keep the pages they have modified, as they are likely to make several more updates to them. However any team member that has made changes to a page would have to forward that modified page to other members when that page is requested by another team member. This is *write-back caching* and is the cache coherence mechanism used on modern microprocessors.

Let us see how our legal team would work under the rules of write-back caching. Robert starts by getting copies of pages seven through ten. He announces to all the others that he has done so. Next Janice get pages eight through ten and announces to all members that she has done so. Robert, Patty, and Tom check their copies of pages to see if they have a local copy of any of the ones Janice has fetched. Robert sees that he does and makes a notation on his copies of pages eight through ten that they are shared, and he also lets Janice know that he has copies of those pages. Janice now marks her copies of pages eight through ten as shared with someone else. Note that Robert is the only one with a copy of page seven, and it is exclusively in his office (cache) as long as no one else fetches a copy.

When Robert is ready to make his updates and starts with page ten, he sees that it is shared with someone else. So he announces his intention to modify page ten and then must wait for a response from the rest of the team. All the others check their copies of the pages and destroy their copies, as none of them has made any changes to their local versions. So Janice throws away her copy of page ten. Robert now makes the change to page ten and keeps it with him. At this point he has the most up-to-date contents of that page, so he marks it as having been modified. This modified page is the only version of that page that is up to date in the system; there are no other valid copies at this point. When Janice is ready to make a change to page ten, she goes to the central location to get a copy but also announces to all other team members about her desire to change page ten. Robert, seeing that his modified copy of page ten is the most up-to-date, informs Janice of this. He then gives her his modified copy of page ten, leaving Robert without a copy. Now Janice has the only up-to-date copy of page ten and she can make additional changes to it, or store it in her cache. However she must not destroy it as this is the only copy of page ten that is up-to-date. If Robert and Janice had both decided to update the page simultaneously, then either one of them could have gone first and then handed the modified page to the other for further updates.

Recapping, each team member can hold local copies of pages as long as they keep track of the state of the page in the system. The page can be:

■ **Shared** with one or more members of the team. The team member can destroy their copy of this page at any time if he or she no longer needs it and does not need to inform anyone of that action.

■ **Exclusive** in only one cache. The owner can destroy her copy if she no longer needs it, as this page is up to date in the central location. This exclusive copy of the page has not been updated at this point, but could be updated by the owner of that page without informing anyone else of the change.

■ **Modified** - this page can exist in only one cache. The owner can make further changes to it at will without informing the other team members. The owner must forward the page to anyone else who needs it. If the owner no longer needs the page, then she or he must put it back in the central location as it is the only up-to-date copy.

The team members must communicate with each other to properly share the pages of their document. All of the communication for this purpose is termed *coherency traffic*. However, the team members may also send messages to each other for other purposes. For example, if Janice decides to take a coffee break and invites Robert to join her, messages between them about breaking for coffee would have no bearing on the shared document and would be termed as *non-coherent traffic* in computer parlance.

Tying It All Together

Multiple processor systems operate under very similar rules for sharing data described in our example above. The caches, represented by the team members above, can hold multiple cache lines. Each cache line is typically composed of sixty-four bytes of data and is the smallest entity handled and tracked by the cache—akin to the document page in our example. The cache controller tracks the state of each cache line and marks it as Modified, Exclusive, or Shared and responds accordingly. If a cache line is no longer up to date in a cache, the controller marks it as Invalid. These, taken together, are referred to by their initials as the *MESI* states (pronounced "messy"). The central memory in a computer system is the common repository of the document in our example above. A typical computer system has at least one memory controller that interfaces with the banks of DRAM memory.

Anatomy of a Multiprocessor System

A typical single processor system is composed of a processor, a memory controller hub (MCH), and an I/O controller hub (ICH). The processor, with its internal cache, is connected to the memory controller with a system interface bus. The memory controller in turn is connected to the I/O controller using another bus designed for that purpose. The system interface bus carries the requests from the processor to the memory controller and the I/O controller. Each request consists of a command or action to be performed, an address of the location in memory or I/O, and optionally data if it is an operation to write out data. This typical single microprocessor based computer system is illustrated in Figure 1.1.

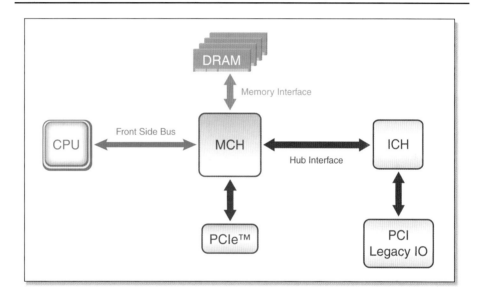

Figure 1.1   Single Processor Computer System Based on the Front Side Bus

The Intel Pentium Pro multiprocessor system, introduced in the mid-1990s, connected as many as four processors on the system interface bus to the memory controller, as shown in Figure 1.2. This FSB added the capability to manage cache coherence between the processor caches using the write-back protocol.

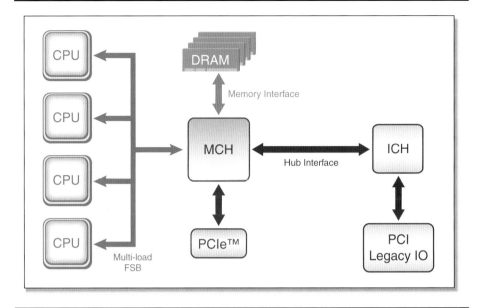

Figure 1.2 Four Processor Computer System Based on the Front Side Bus

The system interface between the CPUs and the MCH operates in a manner very similar to our example of the legal team described earlier. The details of a simple request for data are as follows:

A processor requests data from memory over the Front Side Bus. All the other processors observe this request go by as the FSB connects them all together. These processors check their caches to see if any one of them has a copy of the cache line being requested. This operation of checking the caches of adjacent processors is dubbed a *snoop* in the cache coherence protocol. The term *probe* is also used to describe this operation.

The snoop can produce one of several results depending upon the status of the line in that cache. If the cache does not have a copy of the line being requested, then the cache takes no action. The memory controller will provide the data to the requesting processor. If none of the caches in the system have the data, then the requesting processor places the data in its cache and marks it as Exclusive.

If the requested cache line is in any cache in the Shared or Exclusive state, the cache with the line in that state signals as such on the FSB. If a cache has the line in the Exclusive state, that cache changes its state to Shared.

The memory controller returns the cache line data to the requesting processor, which places the cache line into its cache in the Shared state because one or more caches have indicated that they also have copies of that data.

If the cache line is in the Modified state in the snooped cache, then it signals as such on the FSB. The memory controller recognizes this signal and does not return data. Instead the cache that has the Modified line places the data on to the bus and sends it to the processor requesting the cache line. That cache then marks its own copy of the line as Shared. The receiving processor puts the data in its cache and also marks it Shared. The memory controller simultaneously takes a copy of the data and writes it into system memory.

The rules of operation define similar sequences for all caches to follow where they want to modify data in a cache line or evict the line from the cache to system memory if the line has been updated. These rules are identical to those followed by the legal team when they needed to change the contents of a document page.

It is important to point out that if the rules of operation are correctly defined, and all devices properly follow those rules, then certain characteristics will be ensured. In particular any given snoop will result in all caches responding with either:

■ No hits - no Shared, Exclusive, or Modified copies

■ A single hit - a single Exclusive or Modified copy

■ Multiple hits - all Shared

■ Or the final option, at most one hit-Modified.

Under no circumstances would multiple caches signal a hit-Modified condition and attempt to simultaneously write their Modified lines to the same location in memory.

Evolution to a Link based System

The Front Side Bus works well and offers a simple and elegant solution for multiple processor systems. As computer systems speed up, driven by improvements in processor architecture, silicon technology, and memory technologies, the FSB is operated at a faster rate in order to keep up with the data rates required for a balanced system. This approach has worked well for over a decade through at least five generations of processor evolution at Intel, starting with the Intel Pentium Pro, and continuing beyond the Intel Pentium 4 to the most recent (2009) Intel® Atom™ family of processors.

However, the approach of constantly increasing the data rates on the FSB will eventually encounter some practical considerations that result in diminishing returns for the efforts or costs involved in attaining the faster speeds. Pushing the FSB to operate at data rates faster than 800 megatransfers per second (MT/s), while still having five electrical loads (devices) on the bus, becomes very problematic. An alternative approach was to reduce the number of loads per bus, first to three and eventually to two. With this approach, the FSB rates were pushed up to 1000 and eventually 1600 MT/s (in certain products). Figures 1.3 and 1.4 show the system configurations through these successive steps. To support the four processor configuration of Figure 1.4, note that the memory controller is designed to support four electrically independent FSBs connected to it. One side effect of this is that the memory controller in these systems has over 1500 pins split across four FSBs with 175 signals each. Additional MCH device pins are needed to connect to the memory arrays. This is obviously driving the cost of the MCH device in the wrong direction. Another aspect of these two system configurations is that the entire system memory is behind that one MCH controller.

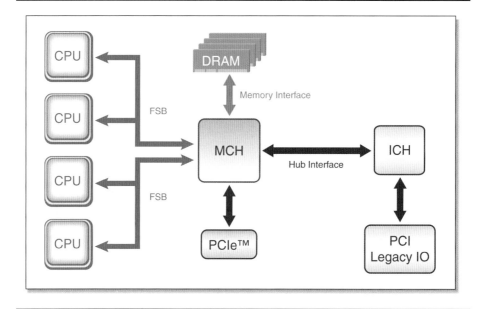

Figure 1.3 Four Processor System with Two Front Side System Busses

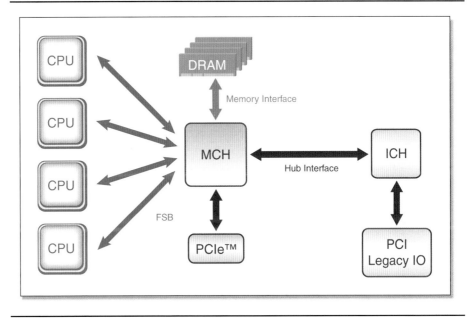

Figure 1.4   Four Processor System with Four Independent System Busses

A System Architecture Transition

Several trends in the evolution of technology made it evident that a fresh look at the entire architecture of a microprocessor system was required. First Intel's latest generation of processors, with multiple cores on a single die, demand ever higher data bandwidth. Multiples of these processors in a system require more memory bandwidth than a single memory controller can economically support. Second, thanks to Moore's Law, it is significantly more economical to integrate memory controllers into the same die as the processors and provide a very modular computational unit. These modular processor/memory controller units can be used to create powerful multiprocessor systems when connected together with an appropriate interconnect interface. The Front Side Bus could have been extended to serve this interface need but would have required significant changes that would render it incompatible with the current systems. Once the architects recognized that the benefits of backward compatibility would have to be sacrificed in any case they decided to take a fresh look at the needs of multiprocessor systems to design an interface with the future in mind.

The key objectives for the new interface were:

■ Significantly Improved Performance and Bandwidth. The goal was to create an interface that would make a radical improvement in system bandwidth and meet the latency goals of the new crop of processors being conceived. The interface also had to readily scalable to meet future bandwidth demands.

■ Software and Processor Family Compatible. The new interface had to be completely transparent to the operating system and user software once the system interface had been properly initialized. Moreover this interface had to be common for future platforms and support both the Intel® Itanium® and Intel® IA-32 family of processors.

■ Low Cost. The interface had to be economical to build on the silicon and in the system boards. An interface with high data rates would make the most efficient use of signals pins and traces.

■ Scalable. The interface had to be architected with an eye on all the possible system topologies of the future that were reasonable to consider and provide the necessary capabilities to support their needs.

■ Power Efficient. The interface had to be power-efficient and meet all the requirements of power control and management capabilities of different platforms.

■ Reliable and Serviceable. This interface was to be used in server systems where reliability and serviceability are key requirements. The interface had to provide the necessary features for robust, error-free operation of the system even in the event of signal interference and disruption. Moreover the interface needed capabilities to support more robust memory systems.

■ Support new capabilities. The architecture of the interface had to provide capabilities and headroom to support new traffic types with different characteristics. This could be media traffic with real time requirements or encrypted streams for advanced security or new commands required to interact with node controllers for more scalable systems.

The Intel QuickPath Interconnect was created to meet all these interface objectives.

Anatomy of an Intel® QuickPath Interconnect System

Figures 1.5, 1.6, and 1.7 show some possible configurations of two-, four-, and eight-processor systems respectively that can be built using the Intel QPI (indicated by the red arrow pairs in the figures). Each processor typically has a memory controller on the same die, allowing systems to be more scalable in performance. However this is not essential and systems can have separate, discrete memory controllers. Similarly, the I/O subsystems can either be incorporated onto the same die as the processors or built as separate I/O hubs. In Figure 1.7 the memory arrays have been left out and the Intel QPI link are depicted as single lines for clarity.

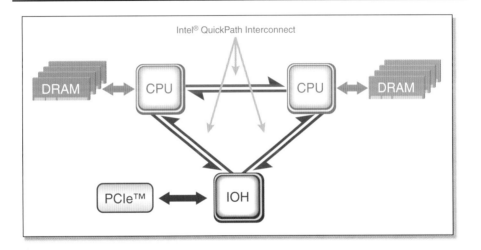

Figure 1.5 System with Two Processors Employing Intel® QuickPath Interconnect Technology

These systems have multiple Intel QPI links connecting the devices to each other. Each one of the links can operate independently of the other links. The performance of such systems can be very high, particularly if the processors are allocated independent tasks, working on data that are optimally distributed across the different memory controllers and close to their own processors. Most current operating systems do recognize such system configurations with Non-Uniform Memory Accesses (NUMA) from each processor and the OS places the data in the memory accordingly.

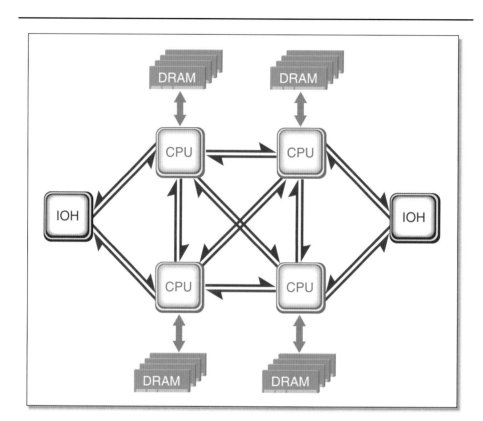

Figure 1.6 System with Four Processors Employing Intel® QuickPath Interconnect Technology

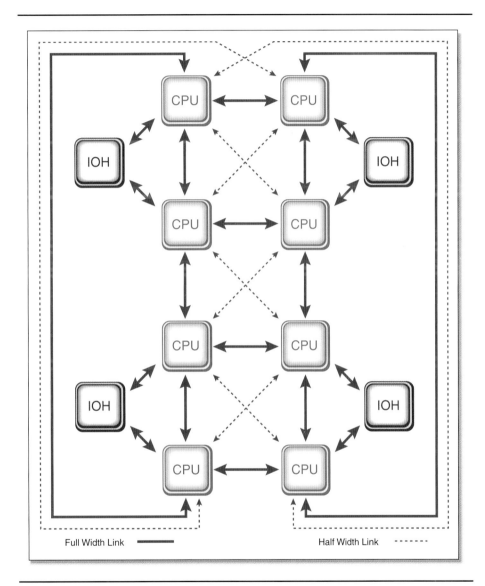

Figure 1.7   System with Eight Processors Employing Intel® QuickPath Interconnect
Technology

The systems shown in Figures 1.5 through 1.7 are fully connected, at least in that each processor has a direct link to every other processor in the system. However, it is possible to build systems using Intel QPI where the devices do not connect to all others. Figure 1.8 shows a four-processor system where each processor uses Intel QPI links to connect to only two other processors.

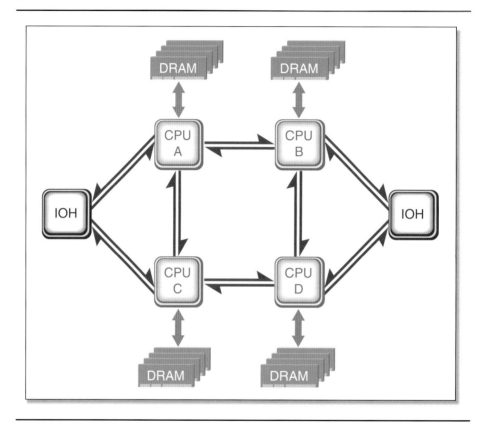

Figure 1.8   Partially Connected System with Intel® QuickPath Interconnect

If CPU A in Figure 1.8 needs to access the memory controller in CPU D, it sends its request through either CPUs B or C, which must in turn forward that request on to the memory controller in CPU D. Similarly, larger systems with eight or more processors can be built using processors with three links, and routing traffic through intermediate processors. Intel QPI routing mechanisms enable such systems to be built. However, systems that are partially connected cannot perform as well as fully connected systems due to the longer latency involved with routing through the intermediate processors and possible bandwidth congestion on the fewer links in the system. Intel QPI also provides mechanisms to help improve the performance of such partially connected systems by reducing the amount of traffic that is created across the links.

Still larger systems can be created by connecting the processors in a hierarchy. Two or four processors could be connected to a *node controller*, forming a cache coherent *node*. Multiples of these cache coherent nodes are connected together using either Intel QPI or some other scalable, coherent interconnect. This approach enables creating systems with many more than 2, 4, or 8 processors. Figure 1.9 illustrates the organization of such systems, which are capable of very high performance on distributable programs. Clearly the operating system must play a large role in distributing tasks to each processor in order to get the highest performance from such systems.

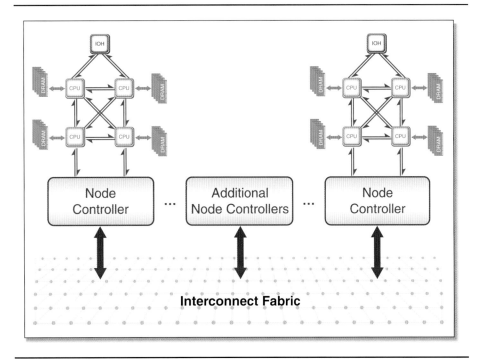

Figure 1.9 Hierarchical Multiprocessor System with Intel® QuickPath Interconnect, Using Node Controllers

Terminology in Systems with the Intel® QuickPath Interconnect

As we dive into the details of systems, it is important to establish a consistent terminology for use throughout the rest of the book. Let's take a look at the types of devices that make up such systems.

There is the processing unit that is usually assumed to be connected to the system interconnect through a high performance cache, and appears as a *caching agent* on Intel QPI. A typical system may have one or more caching agents.

The memory controller is responsible for providing access to the random access memory (RAM) in the system used to store programs and data. A system can have one or more memory controllers where each one covers a unique portion of the total system memory address range. For example, if there are four memory controllers in the system, then each could control one fourth of the entire addressable system memory. The addresses controlled by each controller are unique and are not duplicated on another controller. In Intel QPI terminology, a portion of the memory controller performs the *home agent* function for that particular range of memory addresses. A system would have at least one home agent per memory controller, possibly more than one.

Some devices in the system are responsible for connecting to the input/ output subsystem. They are referred to as *I/O agents*.

One or more devices are responsible for providing access to the code required for booting up the system. These devices are called *firmware agents*.

Depending upon the function that a given device is intended to perform, it may contain caching agents, home agents, and/or I/O agents in a single component. In fact multiple agents of each type may exist within a single device. We have been using the term *processor* (or sometimes *socket*) to refer to the main processing elements in the system. Processor devices typically contain at least one home agent, one caching agent, as well as their primary cores and cache structures that perform the actual instruction set execution.

The connection between two Intel QPI devices is termed a *link* and is composed of a set of unidirectional signals transmitted by one device and received by the other. The individual signals within a link are called *lanes*. Multiple lanes operating in parallel form the link. A full bidirectional communication pathway between two devices uses two links working in concert with each other. This is sometimes referred to as a *link pair*.

Layers of the Architecture

Many contemporary communication architectures have been influenced by the Open Systems Interconnection (OSI) abstract seven-layer model of networking. Intel QPI is no exception and has its own layered model. The functions performed by Intel QPI are logically grouped into four different layers, as illustrated in Figure 1.10. These layers encapsulate similar functions together. The different layers of the Intel QuickPath Architecture are:

- **The Physical Layer:** This layer is responsible for dealing with details of the operation of the signals on a particular link between two agents. This layer manages data transfer on the signal wires, including the electrical levels, timing aspects, and logical issues involved in sending and receiving each bit of information across the parallel lanes.

- **The Link Layer:** This layer is responsible for handling flits of information, as given to and from the link layer and the physical layer, into complete messages. The link layer also manages the flow of these messages and handles errors that may occur during their transfer on that link.

- **The Routing Layer:** This layer is responsible for ensuring that messages are sent to their proper destinations. If a message handed up from the link layer is destined for an agent in another device, this layer forwards it to the proper link to send it on. All messages destined for agents on the local device are passed up to the protocol layer. The implementation details of this layer will vary from one type of device to another. For example, processors that are not required to route traffic from one Intel QPI link on to another may not have a full routing layer.

- **The Protocol Layer:** This layer has multiple functions. The protocol layer manages cache coherence for the interface using the write-back protocol. It also has a set of rules for managing non-coherent messaging. The protocol layer typically connects to the cache coherence state machine in caching agents, and to the home agent logic in memory controllers. The protocol layer also is responsible for system level functions such as interrupts, memory mapped I/O, and locks. One major characteristic of the protocol layer is that it deals with messages across multiple links, involving multiple agents in multiple devices. Lower layers typically deal only with two directly connected devices.

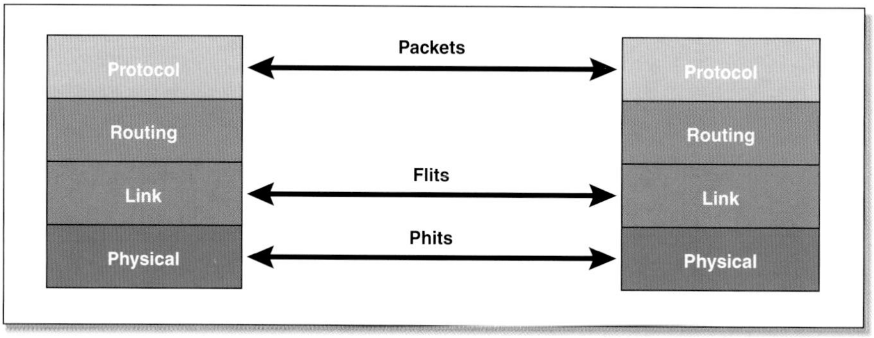

Figure 1.10 Layers Defined for the Intel® QuickPath Architecture

Figure 1.10 also introduces three terms that identify the granularity of the information being exchanged between the layers. These terms are *phits*, *flits*, and *packets*. These terms, and each layer's functions, will be examined in more detail in the following sections and chapters of this book.

Note that this layered architecture allows for a great deal of implementation flexibility and future growth, all within the scope of Intel QPI. The modular approach allows for extensions to be accommodated in an incremental manner. Therefore, in later sections of this text when we talk of certain characteristics of Intel QPI, we are pointing out things that usually reflect current implementations. Those should not be construed as limitations on the overall scope of the Intel QuickPath Architecture. One prime example is the physical layer descriptions. Today a certain set of operational speed or interconnect channel characteristics may be supported. That does not prohibit Intel QPI from evolving into different speeds, communication channels, or even in the types of messages being used.

The Physical Layer

This layer of the interface defines the operation and characteristics of the individual signals of an Intel QPI link. High speed differential signaling is used, with 20 differential pairs in one direction creating one link. A clock lane accompanies the set of 20 data lanes. One link in each direction completes the connection. Figure 1.11 shows the signals of two Intel QPI links, forming a link pair between the two devices.

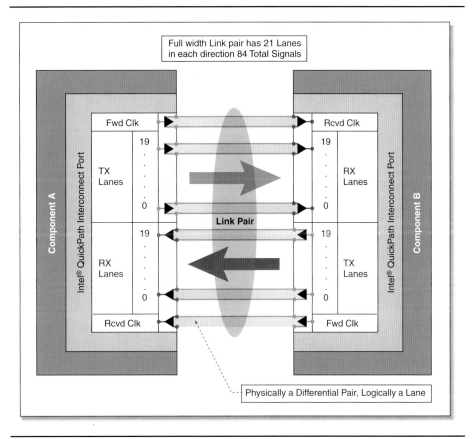

Figure 1.11 Physical Interface of the Intel® QuickPath Interconnect

With the currently defined physical layer, 84 pins are used to carry all the signals of one Intel QPI link operating at its full width. In some applications, the link can also operate at half or quarter widths in order to reduce power consumption or work around failures. The unit of information transferred in each unit of time by the physical layer is termed a *phit*, which is an acronym for physical unit. In the example shown in Figure 1.11, each phit would contain 20 bits of information. Typical signaling speeds of the link in current products calls for operation at 6.4 GT/s for systems with short traces between components, and 4.8 GT/s for longer traces found in large multiprocessor systems.

The physical layer is divided into two sections. The analog or electrical section manages the transmission of the digital data on the traces. This section drives the appropriate signal levels with the proper timing relative to the clock signal and then recovers the data at the other end and converts it back into digital data.

The logical portion of the physical layer interfaces with the link layer and manages the flow of information back and forth between them. It also handles initialization and training of the link and manages the width of operation.

The Link Layer

The Intel QPI link layer controls the flow of information across the link and ensures that the information is transferred reliably. It also abstracts the physical layer into independent *message classes* and *virtual networks* that are required for the upper layers of the interface. We will look at each of these functions of the link layer in some detail below.

Two connected link layers communicate with each other at the granularity of a *flit*, which is an acronym for flow control unit. In Intel QPI, a flit is always 80 bits of information. Every flit contains 72 bits of message payload and 8 bits of CRC. The size of the flit is independent of the width of the physical link. The physical layer manages the transformation between flits and phits transparently. Figure 1.12 shows the subdivision of the 20 possible lanes into four quadrants (labeled Q_O to Q_3 in the figure) of 5 lanes each. Flits are mapped onto the available physical lanes by the physical layer. More details are contained in Chapter 3.

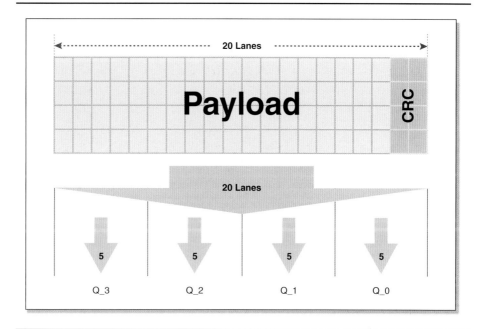

Figure 1.12 Mapping 20 Lanes into Four Quadrants

The link layer handles the flow of data and ensures that only enough data is sent to the link as the receiving agent can accept without overruns. It uses a credit exchange mechanism where the two agents on a link exchange information about the number of buffers (and hence credits) they support. The link layer counts down the credits for each data entity it sends, ensuring it will not overrun the receiver. The receiver returns credits to the sender as it frees up its buffers.

The link layer also ensures that data is transferred reliably across the link. Every flit received by the link layer is checked for errors and groups of flits are acknowledged if they are free of errors. Otherwise the receiving link layer requests retransmission of the flit with errors and all flits subsequent to it that may have been transmitted. Both short transient errors, and burst errors that affect several flits, can be corrected by this means. Moreover, the order of transmission of the flits is maintained.

The link layer abstracts the physical link of Intel QPI into a set of message classes that operate independently of each other. The message classes are very similar to the different types of mail handled by the post office. You can request the post office to send a letter as ordinary first class mail, or registered mail, or even as express mail. You may also have different types of things to send, a letter and a large package for example, and you may wish to use different delivery mechanisms for the different types. Each one of these classes of mail is handled independently of the other, very much like the message classes of the Intel QPI link layer. We will briefly introduce the message classes here, and go into more details of their operation and usage in the next two chapters. The six message classes are: Home (HOM), Data Response (DRS), Non-Data Response (NDR), Snoop (SNP), Non-Coherent Standard (NCS), and Non-Coherent Bypass (NCB)

The link layer extends the notion of message classes to another level. One collection of the six message classes is called a virtual network. Intel QPI supports up to three independent virtual networks in a system. These are labeled VN0, VN1, and VNA. A basic one- or two-processor system can be implemented with just two networks and typically VN0 and VNA are used. All three networks are typically used in multiple processor systems that use the extra networks to manage traffic loading across the links and also avoid deadlocks and work around link failures. The detailed use of these networks is described in later chapters.

The Routing Layer

This layer directs messages to their proper destinations. Every packet on an Intel QPI link contains an identifier of its intended destination. The routing layer logic contains a number of routing tables that indicate which physical link of a processor is the best route to a particular destination. These tables essentially reflect the physical topology of the system. Whenever the link layer hands a message to the routing layer, the routing layer looks up the destination address in the tables and forwards the message accordingly. All messages directed at caching or home agents in a local component are sent to corresponding internal elements. Messages destined for agents in other sockets are sent down the appropriate Intel QPI links identified in the tables.

The routing tables are set up by the firmware when the system is first powered up. Typical small systems will usually run with these values unchanged. Multiprocessor systems typically have more elaborate routing tables that contain information about alternative paths to reach the same destination. These can be used to help redirect traffic around a link that is heavily loaded. Fault resilient multiprocessor systems can also use this information to work around failures in one or more links.

The routing layer can also help to partition and reconfigure multi-processor systems into several smaller systems that logically operate independently of each other while sharing some of the same physical resources. Intel offers Xeon® and Intel® Itanium® processors for high reliability servers that implement several of these features in their routing layers.

The Protocol Layer

The protocol layer is the highest layer in the Intel QPI hierarchy. A primary function of this layer is to manage the coherence of data in the entire system by coordinating the actions of all caching and home agents. The protocol layer also has another set of functions to deal with non-coherent traffic. Intel QPI uses the MESI protocol for cache coherence, but also adds a new state labeled *Forward* (F) to allow fast transfers of Shared data. Hence the term MESIF better identifies the coherent protocol.

Intel QPI offers flexibility in the way cache coherence is managed in a typical system. Proper cache coherence management is a responsibility distributed to all the home and cache agents within the system; each has a part to play. There are some operational choices that can be made. Cache coherence snooping can be initiated by the caching agents that request data, and this mechanism is called source snooping. This method is best suited for small systems that require the lowest latency to access the data in system memory. Larger systems can be designed to rely upon the home agents to issue snoops. This is termed the home snooped coherence mechanism. The latter can be further enhanced by adding a filter or directory in the home agent that helps reduce the cache coherence traffic across the links. Let us look at each of these methods of handling cache coherency and revisit our legal team to see how they would use each one of these mechanisms for their work.

A quick recap is in order. Our legal team of Robert, Janice, Patty, and Tom are all collaborating on a common document. They can keep local copies of the various pages of the document and in our analogy they operate as the caching agents in an Intel QPI based computer system. Mary handles the repository of the entire document and is therefore serving as the home agent.

The team decides that time is of the essence and they should come up with a mechanism that lets them get at the pages of interest as quickly as possible. So when Robert decides he needs page eleven of the document, he asks Mary for a copy from the central repository. However, he simultaneously sends messages to each of his peers to see if they might have copies of the page. If any one of them has a Modified copy, that person will send it to Robert and let Mary know she or he has done so. So Robert gets the page in two messages or *hops* in Intel QPI terms. This is the source snooped method of managing cache coherence, as the source of the requestor for data also sends snoop messages to all peer caching agents.

This is a good time to revisit the Forward (F) state. In the example above Robert requests page eleven from Mary and lets each peer know that he is looking for that page. Normally if any one of Robert's peers had the page in the Shared state they would let Mary know of that fact and Mary would send a copy of the page to Robert. This would take a while as Mary has to go through the entire repository to find the page, not unlike the long access time to read the contents of DRAM in a computer system. However, suppose Patty does have a copy, she can send it directly to Robert as she can very quickly look for it in her small stack of cached pages. If both Patty and Tom had copies of page eleven, one of them would be marked as the designated Forwarder so that Robert would not get two copies of the same page. The Forward (F) state is used to designate <u>one</u> of the caching agents (among those with data in the Shared state), as the one responsible for forwarding data on to the next requestor. This reduces the time to get data to the destination and therefore improves system performance.

The team can use an alternate method where Mary at the repository of all the pages is responsible for checking with all the others for any cached copies of pages. So when Robert requests a page from Mary, she first sends snoop messages to all of Robert's peers to see if any of them have a copy of page eleven. If none of them do, they let Mary know of that fact by their own messages and Mary can send the page to Robert from her central repository. However, if Janice had a copy of the page and she had changed it, Janice would send it directly to Robert and let Mary know she has done so. Janice would also let Robert know that she has kept a copy of the page so that Robert can mark his copy of the page as Shared. In this example Mary had to initiate all the snoops, meaning she was using a home snooped approach, and the page reached Robert after three hops.

Let us extend our example a bit and introduce the notion of a directory. Tom is called on to travel on a business trip and he takes his copies of the pages of the contract with him. When Robert requests page eleven from Mary, then Mary has to ask all the others for the status of their caches regarding page eleven, just as before. However, contacting Tom takes a long time and this is becoming a bottleneck for the whole team. So Mary decides that she is going to keep a list of what pages she has handed out to whom—in effect creating a directory of the state of sharing of pages of the document. So when Robert requests page eleven, Mary checks her directory and immediately knows whom to contact about that page. If Mary's directory indicates that Tom does not have a copy of page eleven, she can give Robert the copy of the page and let him proceed with his work. The directory is an excellent way to reduce the number of snoops that have to be sent across the system. A directory can also be used to manage traffic to agents with long latencies such as those in remote nodes in large systems with multiple nodes. Intel QPI provides all the rules necessary to create such systems, and have them operate effectively.

Our examples above lay out the basic mechanisms of cache coherence management in Intel QPI. We will go into more details of these mechanisms in subsequent chapters.

Performance of the Intel® QuickPath Interconnect

Intel QPI is designed to provide very high system performance over a wide range of system configurations and workloads. It provides an excellent range of capabilities and permits the component designers to select the features that are best suited for their target systems.

High performance small scale systems such as workstations and compute intensive desktop machines tend to benefit from the low latency and high efficiency of the source snoop cache coherence mechanism. This variant of the snooping mechanism is designed to provide data to the processors with the lowest latency possible, as it requires the fewest number of hops across the links. A source snooping approach also takes advantage of the low latency of cache accesses to emphasize forwarding data from one processor to another, rather than getting the data from slower DRAM memory systems. This reduces latency by about 25 percent over comparably sized home snooped systems, producing a significant performance benefit.

Server systems benefit from large memory capacity and high memory bandwidth that can be readily shared across the multiple processors in the system. Intel QPI provides efficient mechanisms to handle data traffic from multiple memory controllers. Very high system throughput is achieved by pipelining a very large number of transactions between the processors and the memory controllers, and handling those transactions simultaneously and independently. Such systems can benefit from the home snooped mechanism of Intel QPI where system bandwidth can be further optimized with snoop filters or directories built into the memory controllers. This behavior allows the home agent, or the memory controller, to keep track of the agents that have requested a particular cache line, and only query them in order to cut down on traffic for cache coherence resolution. Product designers can choose from a wide range of snoop filter or directory mechanisms to help reduce the traffic across the links. The Intel QPI coherence protocol provides considerable flexibility in this area.

Larger system configurations with tens of processors can also be readily built in a hierarchical manner. Groups of two to eight processors and a node controller can be connected to other such nodes, where the node controllers are tied to each other over a set of links. Such a system configuration of two tiers of interconnect is shown in Figure 1.10 The second level of interconnect between node controllers may use Intel QPI, that is a platform architectural decision. Alternatively, an existing protocol can be used between nodes while Intel QPI is used for connectivity within the node. Such systems can take advantage of relatively inexpensive mass-produced processors to build massively parallel computing systems that can take on very large computing problems that require access to shared memory. Such node controllers can also incorporate sophisticated traffic filtering algorithms, taking advantage of the rich and flexible protocol of Intel QPI.

Reliability of the Intel® QuickPath Interconnect

Intel QPI is designed to meet the demands of server systems where a premium is placed upon reliability, availability, and serviceability (RAS). The architecture offers several levels of error detection across the links and provides methods to correct those errors on the fly. However, if errors are seen repeatedly on one or more links, Intel QPI has the capability to isolate the faulty lanes or links and work around the failed elements. Intel QPI has mechanisms to try and recover from routine transient errors.

Intel QPI systems also may support memory mirroring where multiple memory controllers are paired together to provide a more reliable memory storage capability. Intel QPI handles all the traffic appropriately and ensures that data is properly delivered reliably to both the memory controllers in the mirrored pair. In the event of the failure of one of the controllers, the system can continue operation by seamlessly drawing upon the data from the partner controller. The Intel QPI interface can indicate the occurrence of such a failure and permit replacement of the failed memory unit as the links provide the capability to support hot-plug of devices. In all cases, the goal is to keep the system up and running even in the face of several link failures.

Deployment of the Intel® QuickPath Interconnect

The Intel QuickPath Interconnect is the backbone of the next generation of platforms from Intel. Intel QPI is used to tie the processors and the I/O hubs together into single, dual, and multiple processor systems. Intel offers a range of processors and I/O hubs that utilize a varying number of Intel QPI links, The number of links implemented on a device depends upon the specific product requirements the device is intended to meet. This interconnect is used in both the IA-32 architecture and the Intel® Itanium® families of processors. Some of the processors will utilize the source snooped behavior for high performance computing applications that require low latency. The Intel® Itanium® product family and future high end processors designed for large multiprocessor server systems, tend to favor the home snooped behavior as they will focus on scalability and high system bandwidth. The I/O hubs serve the needs of both the small high performance systems and large servers, where multiple I/O hubs in a system can provide the required levels of connectivity.

System designers who want to build large systems can do so using node controllers to tie together clusters of processors. These clusters could have from two to eight processors connected to a node controller. These node controllers can be designed and built by the companies offering large systems and tailored to the specific goals of that system. Intel has enabled a third party to develop a macro cell of the Intel QPI physical layer. This macro cell has been tested and validated to work with certain Intel products. This macro cell is available through an ASIC design company and can be used as part of semi-custom components such as node controllers.

The Intel QPI coherence protocol is flexible in nature and works well to connect heterogeneous devices such as compute accelerators and graphics engines. The interface provides high bandwidth and uniform accessibility to the entire memory address space that can be readily cached by any of the engines. This helps keep software simple.

Parties interested in undertaking a component development using the Intel QuickPath Architecture should contact their Intel representative for more information. Describing such a project is well beyond the scope of this book.

Designing with the Intel® QuickPath Interconnect

Intel QPI brings about a fundamental change in the design of systems and platforms. This is a very significant departure from the Front Side Bus system approach and requires a shift in thinking and new methods and techniques to analyze and observe system operation for performance tuning and debugging. In systems based on Intel QPI, traffic travels across multiple links to multiple memory controllers all working in loose concert with each other. Thus anyone modeling system operational behavior for performance analysis purposes must understand the nature of the interactions between the various elements. As an example, two processors in a multiple link system can issue transactions to different memory controllers down two different links. Although each of these transactions can be considered to be essentially independent of the other, they may share resources within the processors and create snoop traffic on adjacent links.

Similarly, trying to observe the transactions of a single processor for the purpose of tracking down an anomaly requires integrating information from several locations in the system to create a complete picture. The high speed signaling technology of the Intel QPI links cannot be observed by a direct electrical connection to the signals. Intel, working with logic analyzer vendors, has created solutions to provide a way to observe these signals directly or indirectly. Several such probes are required to observe the transactions across many links while debugging a multiple processor system. The user then integrates information from all these sources to get a complete picture of the transactions in the system. All this is a significant departure from the methods used in FSB systems where one can observe all the system traffic on one logic analyzer connected to the bus.

Summary

With its high-bandwidth and low-latency characteristics, the Intel Quick-Path Interconnect advances the processor bus evolution, unlocking the potential of next-generation microprocessors. Intel QPI provides robust error detection and correction for reliable operation of the interconnect. The two-hop, source snoop behavior with cache line forwarding offers the shortest request completion in smaller scale mainstream systems, while the home snoop behavior allows for optimizing highly scalable servers. With all these features and performance it's no surprise that numerous vendors are designing innovative products around this interconnect.

Chapter 2

Intel®
QuickPath Interconnect
in Operation

What I cannot create, I do not understand

—Richard Feynman

In this chapter we take a closer look at the operation and behavior of a system based upon the Intel® QuickPath Interconnect (Intel® QPI). We start with a simple system consisting of two processors and an I/O hub connected together with Intel QPI links. Then we expand the discussion to systems with three processors and discuss the details of device interactions as they communicate across the Intel QuickPath Interconnect.

Life of an Intel® QuickPath Interconnect Transaction

A computer system with two processors and based upon Intel QPI may use the architecture shown in Figure 2.1.

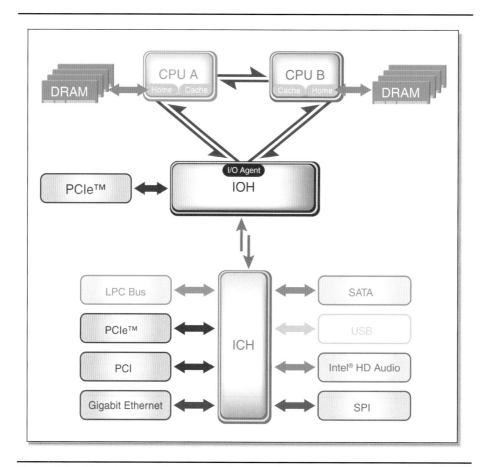

Figure 2.1 Two-Processor System Based on Intel® QuickPath Interconnect Technology

This system is built around two processors where each has an integrated memory controller and two Intel QPI ports. The other key element of this system is the I/O hub (IOH for short) that provides connections to PCI Express™ (PCIe™) and to other chipset elements that provide connections to the USB, SATA, LPC and other busses. The processors and IOH devices are connected together by Intel QPI links.

From the point of view of the Intel QPI operational flows, the system is composed of two caching agents, one in each of the processors. There are also two home agents associated with the two memory controllers, and one I/O agent in the IOH. The interconnect treats the home agent and caching agents as two logically independent entities even though they are implemented on the same processor device. While it is possible for the IOH to also contain a caching agent (and typically it does), the flows presented later will assume the IOH does not have a caching agent. This helps simplify the discussion and is suitable for our purposes in this text.

System Address Spaces

This system has a number of different types of entities that can be accessed by the processors, such as the system memory, I/O devices on the peripheral busses, and control registers in the IOH. Each of these entities may have different characteristics in the way it behaves in the system. Intel QPI provides multiple different address spaces to manage access to these entities in the system. The most commonly used address spaces are:

- **Non-coherent memory:** This region of system addresses is not kept coherent by the hardware mechanisms provided in Intel QPI. A special set of non-coherent transactions are used to access these regions. Requesters normally do not place the data from this region into their caches. Cacheable accesses to these regions may cause a fault depending on the platform behavior. If data from this memory region is put into caches, then it is software's responsibility to maintain cache coherency for this data.

- **Coherent shared memory:** This indicates a memory region that is kept coherent by the Intel QPI hardware cache coherency mechanism with respect to all caches in a coherency domain. Accesses to these regions use coherent Intel QPI transactions. Data from these regions can be put into caches. A requester may choose to access these regions with non-coherent transaction based on some access attributes, for example, based on attributes of PCIe transactions on an I/O proxy entity. However, in such cases the entities rely on the software to maintain coherency between different entities accessing the memory location.

- **Memory mapped I/O:** This indicates regions that map to location on I/O devices and are accessible through the same address space as main memory. Accesses to these regions use non-coherent Intel QPI transactions. Cacheable accesses to these regions are avoided and such accesses may cause a fault depending on the platform settings. Access to these address regions may have side-effects and requesters do not make speculative access to location in these regions unless the location is known to be free of side-effects.

■ **I/O Port:** This indicates regions that are accessible through the I/O port address space of a processor. A system may also use part of its memory space to embed I/O port address space. Accesses to these regions use non-coherent Intel QPI transactions. Cacheable accesses to these regions are not allowed and may cause a fault depending on the platform settings. All requesters in a system have an identical mapping of regions with this attribute in terms of the address range and the target.

■ **Interrupt and Special Operations:** This indicates address regions that are used to perform miscellaneous system functions, such as interrupt delivery and other special operations. All requesters in a system have an identical mapping of regions with this attribute in terms of address range and the target. Some agent that may never generate these accesses may not map these regions. Processors, I/O agents, or configuration agents are targets depending on the type of operation. Access to these address regions may have side-effects and requesters do not make speculative accesses to any address in these regions.

Protocol Messages

Intel QPI provides a range of protocol messages that are tailored to access these various types of address spaces. The Intel QPI protocol layer is sub-divided into two classes, the Coherent Protocol and the Non-Coherent Protocol. The Coherent Protocol describes the behavior of caching agents such as processors and any I/O agents that have caches in them and home agents such as memory controllers with protocol engines that handle reads and writes to a piece of coherent shared memory. All other protocol operations are considered part of the Non-Coherent Protocol. This covers a wide range of topics, including configuration, I/O, interrupts, and non-coherent memory.

Intel QPI agents communicate with one another via messages. At the protocol layer, a message is simply a collection of fields, each of which contains a value or a symbol. Intel QPI agents may communicate with each other over any physical medium that correctly delivers the contents of protocol messages between the agents. Each protocol layer message is mapped to a packet in the link layer which, in addition to the message's fields, also contains information specific to the link layer required for reliable delivery of the messages.

The messages of the protocol layer are divided into six classes that are treated as independent channels between two agents. These message classes were introduced in the previous chapter and are summarized here:

- **Home (HOM)** This class carries requests from a caching agent to a home agent, and it carries snoop responses from caching agents to the home agent. Regardless of the source of the message, the destination is a home agent. Messages in this class are ordered on a per address basis and this is the only class with this requirement.

- **Snoop (SNP)** This message class carries snoop request packets to caching agents. The source can be either another caching agent, or a home agent, depending on the snoop behavior of the system.

- **Non-Data Response (NDR)** This class is used by the protocol layer to send short response messages.

- **Data Response (DRS)** The DRS class is used by the protocol layer to send response messages with data. DRS class messages can contain up to a cache line data payload. DRS class messages can be generated from, and targeted to, both caching agents and home agents

- **Non-Coherent Bypass (NCB)** The NCB class is used by the protocol layer for non-coherent data writes, and several special messages. The NCB channel can contain up to a cache line size payload. The destination of these NCB transactions may be a home agent. NCB is also used to send some forms of messages and interrupts to agents other than the home agent.

- **Non-Coherent Standard (NCS)** The NCS class is used by the protocol layer to send non-coherent Reads and Special Write commands. Most types of requests that do not require cache coherent operation use this message class.

The Home and Snoop channels are used to carry messages for the cache coherent protocol while the Non-coherent Bypass and Non-coherent Standard channels are used exclusively for the non-coherent protocol.

The two response channels are shared between the two protocols. Command messages in the Home channels are ordered on a per address basis between the agents at the end points.

The link layer creates no dependency between any two packets in different message classes. It does not block the flow in one message class because of the blockage in another and treats each message class as independent of all others.

Intel QPI uses these message classes to issue different types of messages. The essential set of messages for normal operation of Intel QPI systems is:

- **Requests** These messages are used to initiate Read or Write actions on Intel QPI. These messages are always sent in the Home message class described above.

- **Snoops** These messages are used by the cache coherence protocol. They are issued by either caching agents or home agents to check other caches for information. Regardless of which agent type issues the snoops, they are always sent to a caching agent. These messages are always issued in the Snoop message class.

- **Snoop Responses** These messages are issued by the caching agents in response to snoops that they receive. These messages are also an essential part of the cache coherence protocol of Intel QPI. These messages are issued in the Home message class and travel to the home agent.

- **Data Responses** These messages are issued by the home agents when they are returning data to the requester. They may also be issued by a caching agent. These messages use the Data Response message class and always carry up to a full cache line of data.

- **Completions** These messages are used by the home agents to complete transaction that do not need to transfer data. These messages are issued in the Non-Data Response channel.

- **Non-Coherent messages** These messages are the basis of the Non-coherent protocol. They are issued in either the Non-coherent Standard or Non-coherent Bypass message classes.

Other messages are available for housekeeping, debug and error recovery. For more details about these messages please see the discussions in Chapter 3.

The Notion of Node IDs

One of the key concepts in Intel QPI is the identity of each element in the system. All Caching agents, Home agents, I/O agents, and so on are assigned their own Node IDs. The value of the Node ID for each system agent is assigned to it at the time of system initialization. Node IDs are used to direct messages to the agents and each message carries the Node ID of the source and destination of the message for proper routing and delivery.

In a typical dual processor system with integrated memory controllers and an IOH each one of the processors, or more accurately the caches in those processors, are assigned Node IDs. The two memory controllers, each of which is a home agent, have their own node IDs. Lastly the IOH is assigned a node ID that covers all the devices that are connected to it. The IOH is also the Home agent for the boot memory in the system.

Directed versus Broadcast Messages

A Directed message is one that is sent to one particular agent in the system. For example, a Directed message would be used to read an I/O port and would be aimed at the single Intel QPI agent where that I/O device exists. In Intel QPI, all messages are Directed messages in the sense that every individual message has only one final destination. However, there are some higher level functions, such as interrupts or locks, which involve sending a message to multiple destinations. These Multicast or Broadcast messages are intended for simultaneous communication with multiple agents in the systems. A Broadcast message would for example be used to send an interrupt to multiple processors in a system. These types of messages are implemented by sending multiple Directed messages. This is discussed in more detail later in this chapter.

End to End Sequence of Events

The transactions in a computer system are most commonly generated by one of the caching or I/O agents in the system. The memory controllers and I/O hubs are typically the target of the vast majority of the transactions in the system. Only a few types of transactions such as interrupts are directed at the processor cores, rather than being sent to another part of the overall processor device such as a caching or home agent.

Request Generation

Whenever an Intel QPI agent is required to read from, or write data to memory or I/O, the agent creates an internal request to the appropriate address space. A request bound for coherent shared memory first checks the local cache for a valid copy of the data. If that check fails to find the data in the agent's local cache, the protocol layer uses the rules of the Intel QPI cache coherence protocol to obtain the most up-to-date copy of data from the system memory, or from another caching agent in the system. The protocol layer then issues a set of requests and associated responses to complete the operations.

Whenever an agent generates a request, either from the protocol layer or directly from the processor core for non-coherent operations, the request needs to undergo a mapping operation in order to determine its destination on the Intel QPI fabric. Agents generating a request specify the destination in terms of the system address space, but destinations on Intel QPI are determined by a Node ID field embedded in the packets being sent. A piece of logic that exists in every requesting agent is known as the *source address decoder* (SAD). The SAD logic takes into account the nature of messages that are to be issued, uses a lookup table to map from system address to Node ID, and then provides that information to be included in the messages sent out onto the Intel QPI fabric.

Operation of the Source Address Decoders

The source address decoders (SADs) maintain a mapping of the system addresses to the various Node IDs of the agents that handle those ranges of addresses. The SADs in all the requesting agents must be configured in a consistent manner if they rely on the hardware-based coherency mechanisms of Intel QPI to maintain cache coherency. In particular, each memory address (at a cache line sized granularity) must be mapped to one and only one home agent. The properly configured SAD is what ensures that requests for a given address are always sent to the one home agent that deals with that address. The SADs also ensure that a caching agent responding with a snoop response to the home node of a cache line will in fact send that response to the correct home node identifier.

The SAD logic takes the physical address and the request type as input and determines the Node ID of the target for that transaction. It also determines the message class and type based upon the address range and type of request it receives. The SAD uses tables that contain a complete map of each address space in the system to the Node ID of the corresponding agent. The SAD provides the following essential attributes for the message:

■ The Class and Type of the message

■ Node ID of the Requester

■ Node ID of the Target of the transaction

■ Address of the entity being accessed

The SAD is also designed to be aware of the internal structure of the agent initiating the request. It uses this information to determine which Intel QPI link would provide the most direct path to the target of that message. It then forwards the message with all the above attributes to the link layer of the appropriate link. If the address of an access does not match any entry in the SAD, then the access is not performed and the transaction is terminated with an optional error indication. For additional information on Address Decoding, please refer to Chapter 4.

Initiating the Transaction over the Fabric

Once the link layer for a particular link receives the message from the protocol layer, along with the message attributes from the SAD, the link layer composes the entire message that is to be issued onto the Intel QPI fabric. The link layer also adds the other information pieces required for reliable transfer of the message.

Each message leaving an agent in the system is tagged with a transaction ID (TID) that is unique between a sender and receiver. Thus any transaction in a system can be uniquely identified by a global ID that is made up of the requester's Node ID, the receiver's Node ID, and the transaction ID. The requesting agent may use the same transaction ID for two different requests at the same time if they target two different home agents.

The following rules apply to the assignment of Transaction IDs and Node IDs:

- A single Node ID may represent both a home agent and non-coherent target agent.

- When this is the case, then the TID pool is shared among all transactions from a given requester NID.

- At configuration time a requester will be given the maximum number of requests it is allowed to issue to a home node (parameter is MaxRequest).

- Requests destined to any home node will be assigned numbers from the available Requester TIDs for that home. The valid Requester TID values are zero through (MaxRequest -1) inclusive.

- Per Requester/Home Node pair, the sum of all currently active transactions initiated via HOM/SNP/NCS/NCB message classes should be less than or equal to MaxRequest. This is to ensure that the Requester does not overrun the Home agent's buffer pool.

The link layer transforms the message into one or more 80-bit flits. The flits are forwarded to the physical layer. The physical layer is responsible for driving the flits onto the physical media and delivering them to the corresponding physical layer in the receiver. The physical layer breaks the flits into the phits that are then driven onto the signal lanes of the link. The operation of the physical and link layers is covered in detail in Chapter 3. For the purposes of the following transaction flow discussions, we will simply assume that those layers perform their function and deliver the messages between the interacting agents.

The receiving link layer gathers all the flits necessary to create the entire message. It then checks the target Node ID in the message and forwards it on the protocol layer if the message matches the agents own Node ID. The protocol layer determines the nature of the operation that is to be carried out.

In large computer systems with many agents, the source of a request may not be directly connected by an Intel QPI link to the final destination. The messages between these agents can be routed through other agents in between. Whenever an intermediate agent receives a message for another Node ID it forwards the message using the functions of the routing layer. This layer directs the message on to another link on that agent that will send the message on towards its intended destination. Tables in the routing layer identify the most suitable link on which to forward that message. The contents of the message are left completely unchanged by the routing agent and this action of routing is entirely transparent to the sending and receiving agents. This permits multiprocessor systems to be constructed using processors with a limited number of links. For example processors with just two links can be used to build systems with the processors connected together as a ring.

Delivery to the Target Device—the Target Address Decoder Function

The agents that are the targets of transactions have a target address decoder (TAD). This piece of logic takes the physical address and command in a transaction and further decodes them into hardware signals to access the specific device(s) at that physical address. The target address decoder in the memory controller disassociates the physical address into device addresses and control signals to access the data in the specific DRAM devices. Similarly the TAD in the IOH determines which device or controller on what peripheral bus must be accessed for a particular I/O transaction. The target address decoder, just as the source address decoder, is typically programmed at the time of system initialization.

The target address decoder is not required at all agents that are targets of Intel QPI transactions. The need for the target address decoder depends on the capability of the target and the types of transactions serviced by the agent. For example, if the memory controller at a home agent is capable of handling the complete physical address space, no further mapping of physical to device address may be needed. Also, configuration transactions targeted to a memory agent may not need any remapping through the target address decoder.

It is expected that all agents in a system have consistent entries in their source and target address decoders. The consistency of the decoders in the system is the responsibility of the system software and no consistency checking is performed by the hardware, except for detection of certain access violations.

Transaction Completion

In order to complete a transaction initiated by the protocol layer in a requesting agent, the home agent issues a response. It uses the appropriate response message and replies to the sender. This message will at a minimum contain the following attributes:

- **Class and Type** of transaction. In this case it will be issued in one of the response classes and use one of the response types.
- **Node ID of the requesting agent**
- **Transaction ID**. This is the same number as that of the original request.

Upon receipt of this response message the Intel QPI protocol layer can either move on to the next step in a transaction, or complete it entirely based upon the nature of the response. The protocol layer can free up all resources such as data buffers that were held for this transaction. The transaction number can also be reused.

Data and Non-Data Responses

Completion of a transaction can occur with one of two response types on the Intel QPI interface. Messages requesting data from the target, such as Read requests, will produce a Data response. Several types of transactions such as Writes do not return data and a Non-Data response message is returned by the receiver to signal the completion of the transaction. This response is required by the Intel QPI protocol so that the originator can recognize when the transaction is done, and then free up the resources used by the completed transaction. This may also signal the point where any dependent actions that were awaiting completion of that transaction to proceed. For example each Write transaction in a series of ordered Writes to a system agent waits for the completion of the previous Write before the next one can be issued. The response for the first Write triggers the second one, and so on.

Snoop Generation and Responses

Snoop requests and responses are a key element of the Intel QPI cache coherence protocol, as snoop messages are used to determine the state and availability of up-to-date data in caches throughout the system. When using the source snooping behavior, all snoops are issued by the caching agent that initiates a transaction to memory in the coherent address space. When the home snooping behavior is used, all snoops in the system are issued by the home agent that receives a request to access coherent address space.

The purpose of the snoop is to obtain information of the state of the cache in the agent that is snooped. This information is sent to the home agent covering that coherent address space in a form of a Snoop Response. It can also trigger a cache coherence action such as a cache state change, or a data transfer from that caching agent to the requester if the target has more up-to-date data at the requested address.

A snoop request to a caching agent can produce one of several types of snoop responses. The types of snoop responses are:

■ **Response with the cache state** at the end of that transaction. This is the state (MESIF) of the snooped agent's cache at the end of the transaction. No data transfer is signaled by this response.

■ **Response with data forwarding**. The data from the snooped agent's cache is transferred to the requester, and the snoop response signals the snooped agent's cache state at the end of that transaction.

■ **Response with data write-back**. The data in the snooped agent's cache is written back into memory and the response signals the snooped agent's cache state at the end of that transaction.

■ **Conflict Response** indicates that the snooped agent's cache has recognized that there are two transactions targeting the very same coherent address. The race or "conflict" signaled by this response has to be resolved by the home agent responsible for that coherent memory address space.

We will look into the details of using these different messages when we illustrate the flow of different transactions in the following examples.

Examples of Transactions

Operational flows of an Intel QPI system are best illustrated by examples of the different type of transactions. We will discuss the operation of these transactions in a typical small system with two processors as shown in Figure 2.1. We will also expand the operation to cover larger multiple processor systems, which create certain cache coherency scenarios not feasible in two-processor systems. These are typically four-processor systems. Figure 2.2 shows such a fully connected system where each processor (with its internal caching agent) has an Intel QPI link to every processor. Figure 2.3 shows a four-processor system constructed with processors that have three links each, and all processors do not have direct links to all others.

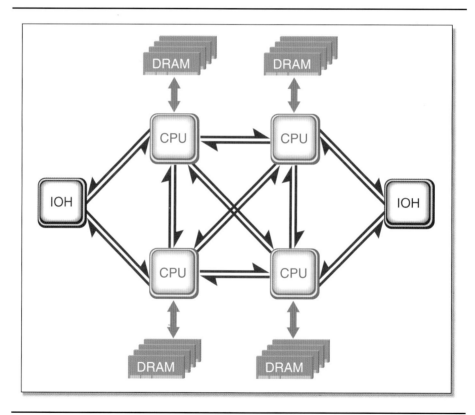

Figure 2.2   Fully Connected Four-Processor System Based on Intel® QuickPath Interconnect Technology

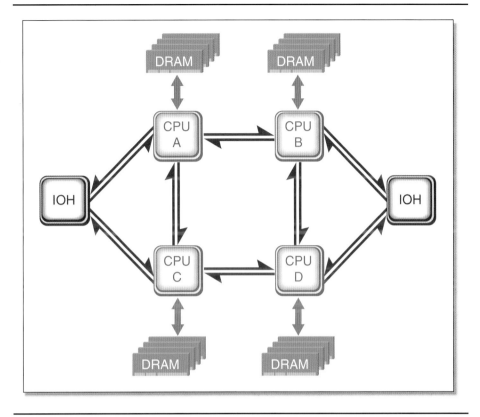

Figure 2.3   Partially Connected Four-Processor System Based on Intel® QuickPath
Interconnect Technology

Processor to Coherent Memory

In this example let us start by examining the sequence of events that take place
when a processor, such as one of those in the two-processor system shown in
Figure 2.1, addresses data in the system-wide coherent memory space. Further
let us assume that these processors are using the source snoop behavior as part
of the cache coherence protocol.

This system is composed of two caching agents represented by the
processors, two home agents associated with the memory controller, and
one I/O agent each with its unique node ID. The two memory controllers
cover the entire coherent address space in the system with non-overlapping

address maps. The source and target address decoders in the system have been appropriately programmed to route messages to the correct agents and memory and I/O devices.

Example of a Read from Coherent Memory

When the first processor in the system makes a request to read data from a particular coherent address, it first checks its local cache. Upon a miss in its cache this Read request is forwarded on to the coherence protocol engine

The requesting agent's coherence protocol engine, in this example following the rules of the source snooping behavior, will send snoops to all the other caches in the system and will also send the Read request on to the home agent. A structure that contains a list of all other peer caching agents in the system is checked, indicating there is one other caching agent (a peer caching agent) in the system. The SAD is used to look up the physical address of the Read transaction, and the SAD contents in this example specify that the address in question is managed by home agent 2, physically located in the other processor device. Using this set of information the protocol engine constructs two messages. The first is a snoop to the peer cache and this message carries information that the requester wants a readable copy of the data at the particular physical address. The second is a Read message to the home agent for that address, in this case home agent 2. Both these messages are forwarded on to the link layer interfacing with the second processor.

The protocol engine in the second processor receives the snoop message and immediately checks the state of its cache for that physical address. One of three outcomes is possible from this inquiry. The three possibilities and the corresponding actions are:

■ **The cache returns Invalid** for that address because it does not have a copy of the data. The cache coherence engine of the snooped cache sends a snoop response to the home agent of that memory indicating that the snooped agent's cache state for that line is Invalid (I).

■ **The cache returns Modified** for that address. This indicates that this cache has the only valid, and modified, copy of the data for that address. The coherence engine then sends two messages, the first to the requester and the second to the home. The message to the requester is a data response with the cache line of data and indicating to the requester that the sender now treats this data as Shared since the sender has kept a local copy of the data. The snoop response message to the home agent indicates that the snooped agent's coherence engine has forwarded data to the requester and has also placed its own cache in the Shared (S) state.

■ **The cache returns Exclusive** for that address. The coherence engine sends a snoop response to the home agent indicating that it has changed the cache state of its copy of the cache data to Shared (S). The home agent then returns the data following the rules described below.

The home agent receives the Read request message from the requester. The type of request and the physical address in the message is forwarded to the Target Address Decoder to identify the exact bank of DRAMs to access in the memory system behind the controller. The memory controller then issues a request to read that particular cache line from memory. The home agent is also aware of the total number of caching agents in the system and hence the number of snoop responses to be received in order to complete this request. In this example of a two-processor system the home agent awaits the arrival of the snoop response from the sole peer agent. Then depending upon the type of snoop response it receives it takes one of the following actions:

■ **An Invalid Snoop Response.** The home agent returns data it has fetched from memory to the requester. It completes the transaction with a Data response message that is sent on the DRS channel.

■ **A Forwarded and Shared Snoop Response.** The home agent recognizes that the cache with this response has forwarded a more up-to-date copy of the data to the requester. The home agent can drop the data it has received from the memory controller and issue a message to the requester that the transaction is complete. This non-data response message is sent in the Non-Data Response channel.

■ **A Shared Snoop Response.** The home agent replies with the data it has fetched from for that address. It completes the transaction with a data response message that is sent on the DRS channel.

Operation of a Read transaction in a multiprocessor system is very similar to the operations described above. However the snoop request from the requester can find one or more of the peer caches in the "shared" state—a situation that is not possible in the example with two processors. In such multiprocessor systems all the peer caching agents that have the data in the Shared state will indicate that fact in their snoop responses to the home agent. They will take no other action regarding their cache state. Upon receipt of this "shared" snoop response the home agent will complete the transaction by reply with a data response and return the data it has fetched from memory.

Message Sequence Diagram Notation

Although we can verbally describe the sequence of operations of various Intel QPI transactions, diagrams are a tremendous help to visualizing the flow between agents. Message sequence diagrams provide a very compact way to visually present these transactions in a way that is easy to understand. These diagrams present the information in a consistent manner and are often used to illustrate flows between Intel QPI agents.

The message sequence diagrams shown in the following sections use the legend shown in Figure 2.4. It is always assumed that all requests in a sequence diagram target a single memory address whose home agent is the one shown in the diagram. Any other home agents in the system do not participate in the transaction being illustrated.

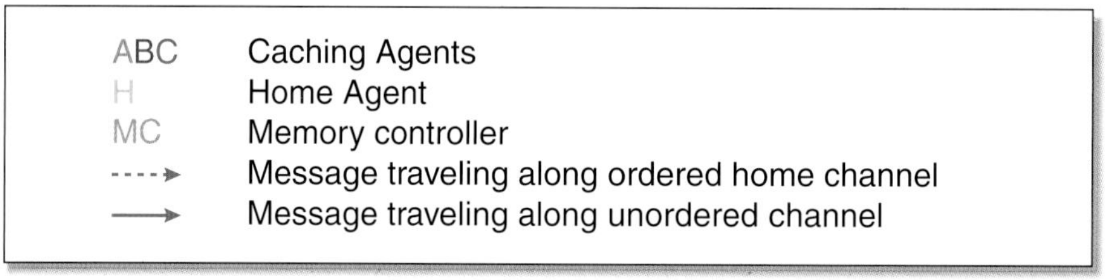

ABC	Caching Agents
H	Home Agent
MC	Memory controller
- - - ▸	Message traveling along ordered home channel
⟶	Message traveling along unordered channel

Figure 2.4   Legend for Message Sequence Diagrams

The diagrams show the advance of time starting from the top of the page and flowing downwards. The initial states of the caches in each of the caching agents are shown at the head of the diagram. As we study the operation of the different types of Intel QPI transactions we will also present them as message sequence diagrams.

Basic Coherent Transaction Illustrations

Let us look at some operations in the form of a message sequence diagram using the notation we described earlier. In the first illustration we look at a Read operation from coherent shared memory in a three processor system. Figure 2.5 shows such a system.

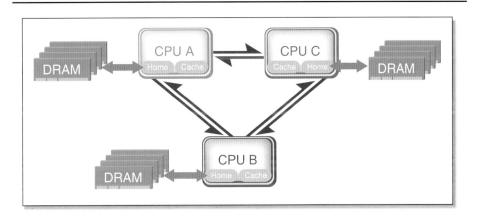

Figure 2.5   Three-Processor System Based on Intel® QuickPath Interconnect Technology

In the second illustration we look at a Write operation to coherent shared memory in the same system configuration. In both cases, the flow begins with a transaction being issued by one of the processors (caching agent) in the system.

Reading from Coherent Memory

Figure 2.6 shows the message sequence diagram for this example. In this case the initial states of the caches in both the other processors are invalid, as indicated on the diagram. Caching agent C has issued the Read request to the home agent on the ordered home channel, as shown by the dashed line. It also issues snoops to each of the peer caching agents on the unordered snoop channel. The snoops carry the information that agent C desires to Read the data (as opposed to intending to modify it, in which case it would have requested ownership).

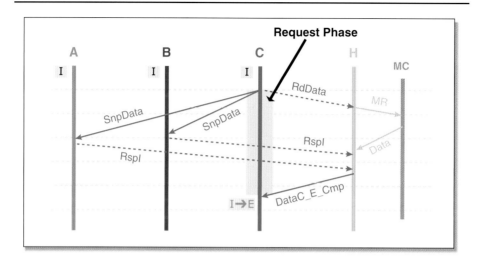

Figure 2.6 Read from Coherent Memory in a Three-Processor System

The request to the home triggers a memory read operation and data is returned to the home agent. It awaits the arrival of the two snoop responses and upon receiving them it forwards the data to the requester. The data response also indicates the Exclusive state as neither of the snooped caches had a cached copy of the data as indicated in their snoop responses.

Note that the order of arrival of the messages at the home agent is unimportant. These messages may be traveling over different links, or one of them may have encountered a transient error and may have been delayed because it had to be reissued by the link layer. The message sequence diagram for this transaction could equally have been the one shown in Figure 2.7 where the one of the snoop responses arrives at the home before the Read request message arrives from the requester. The end result is exactly the same as in the previous diagram.

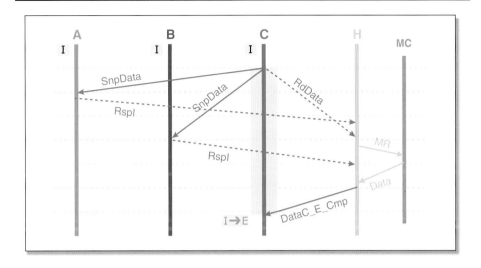

Figure 2.7 Read from Coherent Memory in a Three-Processor System—Another View

Writing to Coherent Memory

Intel QPI uses the write-back cache coherence protocol. This protocol is designed with the underlying belief that a processor will make multiple updates to data entities in close proximity to each other. For example server systems are likely to update several fields in a database record that is stored in a contiguous address space. Thus there is a benefit in fetching an entire cache line of data and making it available for multiple updates in the high speed cache memory.

Following the rules of the coherence protocol the protocol layer will fetch an entire cache line of data into the requester's cache in the Exclusive state, thus ensuring that this cache is the only one with this data in the system. The Write operation will now be carried out in the cache of the requesting agent. Note that the copy of the line in main memory is not "written" to; at least not yet.

Let us follow the sequence of events that take place to carry out this operation. The internal Write request first checks the local cache for the requested data. The four possible outcomes and subsequent actions are:

■ **The cache returns Modified** for that cache line indicating that it has the only valid, and modified, copy of the data at that address. The coherence engine updates the data in the cache with the new Write operation. No further action is necessary and no Intel QPI transactions are generated.

■ **The cache returns Exclusive** for that cache line indicating that it has the only valid cached copy in the system. The coherence engine updates the cache with the data from the Write request and changes its cache state to Modified. Again no further action is required and no Intel QPI transactions are generated.

■ **The cache returns Invalid** for that address as it does not have a copy of the data. The cache coherence engine creates two sets of messages. The first is a solitary message to the home agent requesting data with ownership in the Exclusive state. The second is a set of snoops to all the peer agents again requesting Exclusive ownership.

■ **The cache returns Shared** for that address because it has a copy that also exists in another cache. The cache coherence engine creates two sets of messages. The first is a solitary message to the home agent requesting ownership in the Exclusive state of the data it already has in its cache. The second is a set of snoops to all the peer agents again requesting Exclusive ownership of the cache line.

When the peer set of caches receive the snoops they check the local cache states at this address. The possible states and actions are:

■ **The local cache is Invalid** for that address because it does not have a copy of that data. It returns an Invalid snoop response to the home agent.

■ **The local cache is Shared or Exclusive** for that address because it has a copy of data at that address. The cache coherence engine modifies the local cache state to Invalid and returns a snoop response stating as such to the home agent.

■ **The local cache is Modified** indicating that it is the only cache with the most up-to-date copy of the data. The cache coherence engine forwards the data to the requester and indicates that this data is in the Modified state. It also send a snoop response to the home indicating that it has forwarded the data and changed its local state to Invalid.

The home agent can receive one of two types of requests from the requester.

In the first case the home agent sees a request for data in the Exclusive state. It initiates a memory read at the location addressed by the message. It then awaits the requisite number of snoop responses from the peer caches. If none of them indicate that they have forwarded data to the requester, the home agent replies with a data response to complete the transaction. However if any one of the peer agents has forwarded data to the requester because it had a modified copy, the home completes the transaction with a non-data response and drops the data it had fetched from memory.

In the second case the home agent receives a request for exclusive ownership of data the requester already has in its cache. Here the home agent waits for all the snoop responses from the peer caches indicating that they have transitioned to Invalid. Then the home agent completes the transaction with a non-data response granting exclusive ownership of that cache line to the requester.

The requester can carry out its Write operation upon receiving data in the Exclusive state or upon gaining the Exclusive state for the data it already has in its cache. The updated data is cached in the Modified state where it can be updated as many times as necessary by that processor or until another processor requests access to that cache line.

The sequence of operations for the first case mentioned above is illustrated in Figure 2.8.

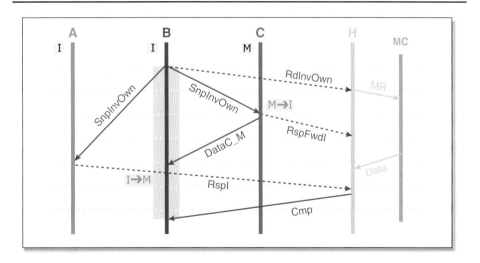

Figure 2.8　Intel® QPI Transaction for Ownership of cache line.

Processor B intends to modify the contents of a cache line and issues the Read_Invalidate_Own transaction to the home agent. Processor C has a modified (M state) copy of that cache line and, upon receiving the snoop request from processor B, forwards the modified data on to processor B and invalidates its own cache copy. Processor C also indicates that it has done so to the home agent via the Response_Forward_Invalidate message. Once the home agent has received this response, and also a snoop response from Processor A, it completes the transaction and discards the cache line it had speculatively fetched from memory.

Home Message Class Commands

All accesses to the coherent memory address space are carried over the Home channel. A range of commands are provided for the different types of transactions, some of which are described earlier. Here is a list of the request commands used to access the coherent address space:

- Read_Code: The command requests data in the Shared state.
- Read_Data: The command requests data in Exclusive state but will accept it in the Shared state.
- Read_Current: This command requests data in the Invalid state
- Read_Invalidate_Own: This command is used to request data in the Exclusive state and will accept a Modified copy
- Invalidate_I_to_E: This command requests Exclusive ownership without data transfer
- NonSnoopRead Request data from memory without regard for coherence
- Invalidate_X_to_I: This command flushes a cache line globally from all the caches in the system
- Evict_Clean: This command is used to evict a clean cache line
- Invalidate_Writeback_M_to_I: This multifunctional command requests Exclusive state for data already in the cache, to modify it and write the line back to memory via a Writeback_M_to_I transaction.

Writeback Marker Messages

The following Writeback marker messages are used to manage cache coherence state and are also sent over the Home channel. Writeback marker messages do not carry data (hence the name "marker"); the data are sent separately via Writeback*Data* messages in the data response (DRS) channels:

- Writeback_M_to_I: Downgrade a cache line from Modified to Invalid and signal an in-flight Writeback_I_Data message.

- Writeback_M_to_S: Downgrade a cache line from Modified to Shared and signal an in-flight Writeback_S_Data message.

- Writeback_M_to_E: Downgrade a cache line from Modified to Exclusive and signal an in-flight Writeback_E_Data message.

- Non_Snoop_Write: Signals an in-flight Non_Snoop_Write_Data.

Core to/from Non-Coherent Memory

A processor may issue transactions to non-coherent memory for one of two purposes. The first is to access data at a DRAM location in system memory without invoking the hardware cache coherence mechanisms of Intel QPI. The second use for these transactions is to access I/O devices that have been mapped to the memory space. Let us look at each in some detail.

A system designer may choose to set aside a certain amount of DRAM memory for special use where the Intel QPI hardware mechanisms should not play. The coherence in this space may be maintained entirely through software. For example memory that is used for high performance multimedia applications may be so designated and shared between a limited number of agents. Intel QPI provides a set of commands for this purpose. These commands are driven over the Home channel and the requester does not issue any snoop requests to its peers. The home agent recognizes the command and completes the Read or Write operation without waiting for any snoop responses.

Mapping I/O devices to a region in the memory address space provides an opportunity to access the devices in this space with a rich and versatile set of commands. These transactions are part of the non-coherent protocol of the Intel QuickPath Interconnect. The most basic read and write operations targeted at these devices are issued from the processor using the Non-Coherent_Read and Non-Coherent_Write messages. Intel QPI also offers variants of these commands, Non-Coherent Read Partial and Non-Coherent Write Partial, which transfer less than a complete cache line's worth of data.

Figures 2.9 and 2.10 show the flows of messages for the non-coherent read and write transactions respectively.

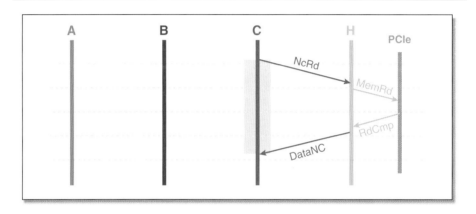

Figure 2.9   Intel® QPI Non-Coherent Read Transaction

A non-coherent read transaction is initiated with a Non-Coherent_Read request. This request is routed through the Intel QPI fabric to the target non-coherent agent that interfaces I/O devices. Since the read request returns data from the I/O device, the target non-coherent agent forwards the read to the I/O domain using the appropriate protocol of that interface. The I/O device eventually returns data to the target non-coherent agent, which forwards this data to the requester using a Data_Non-Coherent response, and the requester deallocates the Non-Coherent_Read. If the non-coherent read was targeting MMIO memory attached (or integrated) to an Intel QPI entity, the target returns the Data_Non-Coherent response after fetching the data from the appropriate memory location (or internal buffer depending on the microarchitecture).

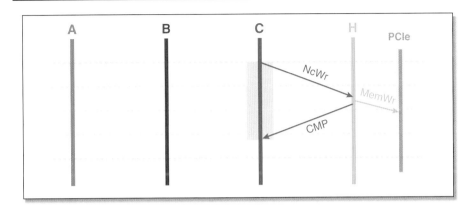

Figure 2.10 Intel® QPI Non-Coherent Write Transaction

A non-coherent write transaction is initiated with a Non-Coherent Write or a Non-Coherent Write Partial request. This request is routed through the Intel QPI fabric to the target non-coherent agent that interfaces I/O devices. The target non-coherent agent responds to the Non-Coherent Write with a Complete response once the write request is guaranteed to preserve the memory ordering model of the platform (for example, the producer-consumer model described in the PCI specification). When the Complete returns to the requester, it deallocates the request and the requester is permitted to issue the next order dependent request. The target non-coherent agent forwards the write to the I/O domain using the appropriate protocol of that interface.

If the non-coherent write was targeting memory-mapped I/O (MMIO) memory attached (or integrated) to an Intel QPI entity, the target issues the Complete response after the data is written to a point of global observation. This is a point in a transaction where the consistency requirements of data are met across the system. On Intel QPI, the flow above is identical for either case.

Intel QPI also permits non-coherent agents to combine successive writes to the same cache line. The fabric differentiates non-coherent writes from write-combinable memory-mapped I/O writes. The latter is initiated through Write Combining Writes or Write Combining Write Partial requests, permitting the target agent (typically an I/O entity) to optionally combine these writes into a longer write, which is further optimized for the I/O interface (for example, PCIe). Write Combining Write transactions can only target memory-mapped I/O space. Figure 2.11 shows the flow of messages and the sequence of operations for write-combining transactions.

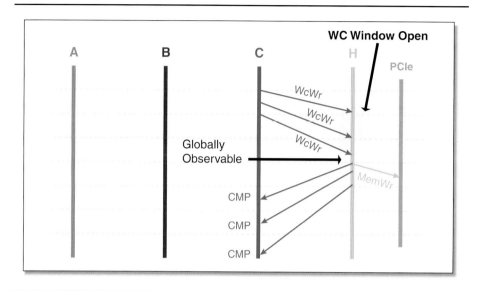

Figure 2.11 Intel® QPI Write Combining Transaction

In general, all rules and flows for Non-Coherent Write and Non-Coherent Write Partial apply to Write Combining Write and Write Combining Write Partial. In addition, the following rules apply:

1. The target of a Write Combining Write or Write Combining Write Partial is not permitted to combine across a 4-KB boundary. Intel QPI write combining requires that an I/O device's address space not cross a 4-KB boundary. This Intel QPI restriction removes the risk of improperly combining independent writes to independent I/O devices or functions.

2. Like Non-Coherent Write and Non-Coherent Write Partial, Write Combining Write and Write Combining Write Partial cannot be completed on Intel QPI until after the write is globally observable (for example, reaches the PCI ordering domain). Since the software fences are not visible on the Intel QPI fabric, processor write combining buffer flushing events are expected to force the buffer contents to be globally

observable. Therefore, the target non-coherent agent cannot complete the write on Intel QPI until it can guarantee global observation (for example, posted in a chipset-posted write queue).

Core to and from I/O

The instruction set of the Intel processors defines a unique I/O address space of 64 kilobytes. Due to legacy reasons on IA-32 architecture systems, legacy I/O space is 64 kilobytes + 3 bytes. The "extra" three bytes are shadows of the first three bytes starting at I/O address 0 and are accessible by issuing an I/O transaction that straddles the 64-KB limit (for example, a 4-byte access starting at address FFFFh).

Figures 2.12 and 2.13 illustrate the I/O Read and Write transactions respectively.

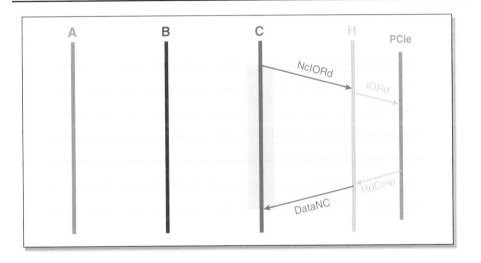

Figure 2.12 Intel QPI I/O Read Transaction

An I/O read transaction is initiated with a Non-coherent_IO_Read request. This request is routed through the Intel QPI fabric to the target I/O proxy that interfaces with I/O devices. The I/O proxy forwards the request to the appropriate I/O interface and does not respond with a Data_Non-coherent response until after the I/O device completes it on its interface. When the Data_Non-coherent returns to the requester, it deallocates the request.

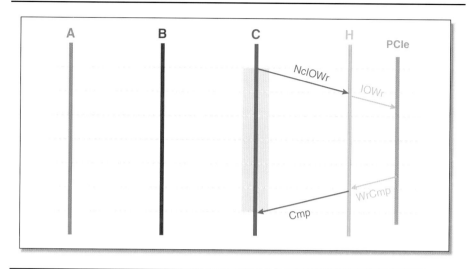

Figure 2.13 Intel® QuickPath Interconnect I/O Write Transaction

An I/O write transaction is initiated with a Non-coherent_IO_Write request. This request is routed through the connecting fabric to the target I/O proxy that interfaces with I/O devices. The I/O proxy forwards the request to the appropriate I/O interface and does not respond with a Complete (Cmp) response until after the I/O device completes it on its interface. When the Complete response returns to the requester, the requester deallocates the request.

The I/O address space is not cacheable and neither the processors nor the I/O devices that are the homes of these addresses will cache the data. The processor instructions that read and write I/O data can address up to 32 bits of data. Hence on Intel QPI the corresponding I/O read and I/O write transactions can transfer 1 to 4 bytes of data and the byte enables are typically contiguous. However, because the I/O address can start at any byte, I/O requests that split across the 8 byte boundary have to be split into two transactions. A requirement falls on the initiator of I/O read and write requests that unaligned transactions are split up into appropriately sized requests. Component designers pay close attention to the ordering of these split-up requests. For example, if a processor core issues an unaligned legacy I/O write transaction, there could be a software expectation that this write occurs in little endian order (lowest byte first), and this is the legacy behavior.

To ensure proper order, agents that split legacy I/O reads and writes should do so by serializing the fragmented requests starting with the low-order portion. Otherwise, the fact that these transactions can pass each other on PCI would cause problems.

I/O to and from Memory

I/O devices in systems based on Intel QPI are supported by an I/O proxy agent that translates all operations from the I/O subsystem into the appropriate transactions on Intel QPI. Typically the I/O devices are the targets of transactions issued by the processors in the system. However the I/O agents can issue read and write transactions to memory to carry out data transfers to the I/O subsystem. These could be normal cache coherent read or write transactions issued by an intelligent I/O controller in the system. Alternately these operations could be direct memory access (DMA) accesses.

Interrupts

Systems based on Intel QPI support the xAPIC and SAPIC interrupt architecture used by the IA-32 architecture and Intel® Itanium® processor family, respectively. The interrupt architecture assumes that there is at least one I/O xAPIC with each I/O subsystem (that also support I/O devices without message signaled interrupts) connected to the Intel QPI network, and each processor has an integrated Local APIC to receive and process interrupts and to send inter-processor interrupts (IPIs). In addition, I/O devices may be capable of generating interrupt messages directly through PCI message signaled interrupt (MSI) or equivalent mechanism. Interrupts, interrupt acknowledgment, and end of interrupt (EOI) are delivered over Intel QPI to the target processor or I/O xAPIC.

Interrupt model for IA-32 Architecture Systems

IA-32 architecture–based systems allow use of either Physical destination mode or Logical destination mode to identify the target processor context. In the Physical destination mode with directed delivery, the interrupt message specifies a unique processor context by setting its Physical APIC ID as the target or by setting broadcast encoding to indicate all processor contexts as targets. The Logical destination mode supports two types of addressing modes: Flat addressing mode and Cluster addressing mode. In the Flat addressing mode, target specified in the APIC ID field of the interrupt messages is interpreted as a bit vector where each bit indicates a processor context. This addressing mode is used only in systems that support eight or fewer processors. In the Cluster addressing mode, the APIC ID field is divided up into the Cluster ID and the Logical ID fields and is used in larger systems with more than eight processors.

Interrupts from I/O devices or inter-processor interrupts (IPI) are delivered on the Intel QuickPath Interconnect using the Interrupt_Physical or Interrupt_Logical request with an address in the interrupt delivery region of the system address map. Part of the address field contains the Local APIC ID of the target processor context for the interrupt.

The interrupt delivery mechanism also supports the lowest priority interrupt delivery mode. The lowest priority delivery mode may be used only with I/O-initiated interrupt messages.

Delivery of interrupts under certain addressing modes and platform configuration relies on the capability to broadcast Interrupt_Physical or Interrupt_Logical requests to all processor entities in the system.

Intel QPI supports interrupt redirection to enable lowest priority interrupt delivery to improve performance through interrupt distribution, taking into account task priority level among processor contexts and other factors. The exact redirection algorithm used in a system is dependent upon the implementation of the agent.

Interrupt Model for the Intel® Itanium® Processor Family

The Intel QuickPath Architecture supports the SAPIC interrupt architecture for use by the Intel® Itanium® processor family. All interrupts in Intel® Itanium® architecture–based systems use Physical destination mode to identify the target processor context for an interrupt and this context is specified within each interrupt message. Only one processor context can be specified as the target in one interrupt message. SAPIC interrupt architecture, unlike xAPIC, does not support multiple target specification through multicast or broadcast interrupts. However the SAPIC supports Directed or Redirectable delivery of interrupts.

The protocol agent initiating an interrupt for Directed delivery uses the Node_ID of the target and sends an Interrupt_Physical request to the target node. The target of the Interrupt_Physical request is responsible for delivering the interrupt request to the corresponding Local APIC identified in the request. The target node sends a Complete response back to the source of the Interrupt_Physical request. The Complete response is generated only after the local APIC has received the interrupt and the interrupt is software visible.

Edge Triggered and Level Sensitive Interrupts

The interrupt mechanism supports both edge triggered and level sensitive interrupts where a level sensitive interrupt is used to signal a condition rather than an event. Both edge triggered or level sensitive interrupts are processed in the same manner at the target processor. However, completion of the servicing of a level sensitive interrupt is signaled back to the device that generated the level triggered interrupt. This is done using an end of interrupt indication.

In IA-32 architecture systems, an End_Of_Interrupt message is used to provide this indication. This message belongs to the Non-Coherent class of requests on the Intel QPI. Once the End_Of_Interrupt request reaches the I/O xAPICs the correct I/O xAPIC recognizes the interrupt vector and checks if the interrupt condition is still active. The I/O proxy entity returns a Complete_Data response and once all the expected Complete_Data responses are received by the requesting processor entity, the End_Of_Interrupt transaction completes. An I/O entity receiving an End_Of_Interrupt transaction is required to order any previous outbound posted write request ahead of the End_Of_Interrupt transaction from the same entity. This is done to make sure that any previous writes to I/O xAPIC that may update redirection table entries is observed before the End_Of_Interrupt is processed.

Conflict Resolution with Example

The Intel QuickPath Architecture is designed for multiple simultaneous operations across all links in the system. The aggregate bandwidth of all the links is available to all the caching agents for the highest system performance. However there are times when two or more caching agents request data from the same physical address in coherent, shared memory almost simultaneously. This creates a conflict, and the Intel QPI rules of cache coherence are designed to handle such situations to ensure data coherency and consistency is maintained.

Figure 2.14 illustrates such a conflict in a two-processor system. The two caching agents A and B both request access with ownership to a cache line as each wants to modify the data. Agent B's request arrives at the home first and triggers a read from memory. Soon afterwards the home receives the request from agent A. The moment a snoop response is received by the home, it forwards the data to the other caching agent. This is because in a two-processor system, the home needs one snoop response from the peer caching agent. Here it has received it from agent B, so it forwards the data to agent A. The data response to A also indicates the existence of a conflict. This response is acknowledged by agent A and the home agent completes the transaction with agent A by sending to agent A a non-data "complete and forward" response. This is a request for agent A to forward the data on to agent B.

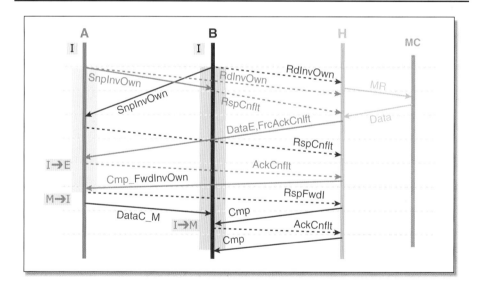

Figure 2.14 Example of Conflict Resolution

The home agent awaits a snoop response from agent A indicating that it has forwarded the data on to agent B and invalidated its own cache. The home agent can now complete the transaction for agent B with a non-data response. Agent B receives the modified data from agent A and the completion from the home; agent B acknowledges this to the home and this finally completes the sequence of events resolving the conflict.

The Forward State Optimization

The source snoop behavior is designed to offer the lowest latency to coherent data for the highest performance on desktop and workstation workloads. Thus a further optimization has been added to the Intel QPI coherence protocol to take advantage of the lower latency of caches and offer a benefit to Read transactions.

Let us recall the earlier example of a Read transaction from coherent memory. In that example a read request is sent to the home agent and Snoop requests are issued to all the peers. They return snoop responses to the home indicating whether any one of them has a copy of the data. However the home agent sends data to the requester and completes the transaction. If one or more of the peers have a copy of the data in their caches, this data potentially could be returned to the requester significantly sooner than from the home agent, which has to fetch the data from slower DRAM memory.

The coherence protocol adds the (optional) Forward (F) state to the existing set of four cache states. This F state is a variant of the Shared state and only one caching agent of the set with Shared data is assigned the Forward state. The caching agent so designated is required to immediately forward its data in response to the read request. Thus the requester receives the data in just two link hops and with the lowest possible latency for that cache line. The caching agent that forwarded the data sends a snoop response to the home agent indicating that it has provided the data, and the home agent in turn can complete the transaction with a Non-Data response.

Only one caching agent at any point in time is assigned the Forward state for a particular cache line. The home agent makes the assignment of the Forward state in its response when it recognizes that no other cache has a copy of that data.

Invalidating Write Flow

The source snooping behavior of the Intel QPI cache coherence protocol supports a special flow called invalidating write (IW). This flow has the special property that allows correct coherence operation even though one of the caching agents, which is called the IW agent and is typically an I/O proxy, never has to be snooped.

Currently the invalidating write (IW) flow has the following restrictions:

■ The IW flow may not coexist with home-snooping flow.

■ There can either be at most one IW agent among the caching agents

The IW flow deviates from the standard source-snooping flows in the following ways:

■ The IW agent is never snooped by non-IW agents (though IW agent may snoop non-IW agents).

■ The IW agent may issue only a subset of the interconnect request types: Read_Code, Read_Data, Read_Current, Invalidate_Writeback_M_to_I, Non-Snooped_Read, and Non-Snooped_Write.

■ The IW agent never caches a line in Shared or Forward state. In particular, any data it obtains via Read_Code or Read_Data is not cached or modified by the IW agent.

■ The IW agent performs all coherent writes using the invalidating write request Invalidate_Writeback_M_to_I, which is in essence the fusion of Invalidate_I_to_E and Writeback_M_to_I into a single transaction.

In the protocol flow diagrams that follow, IW denotes the IW agent, B and C two (non-IW) caching agents, and Home the home agent. Figure 2.15 shows the normal conflict-free flow of Invalidate_Writeback_M_to_I.

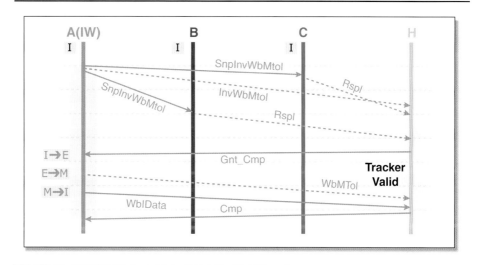

Figure 2.15 Invalidating Write with No Cached Copy

Here the IW agent issues Invalidate_Writeback_M_to_I to home and snoops peer caching agents B and C with Snoop_Invalidate_X_to_I. Both agents B and C reply with Response_I, indicating they have no valid copy of the requested line. So the home grants exclusive ownership (without data) to the IW agent using Grant_Complete. So far the flow is almost identical to that of Invalidate_I_to_E, except that the Tracker entry of the Invalidate_Writeback_M_to_I is not deallocated when the Grant_Complete is sent. After obtaining exclusive ownership, the IW agent writes its write data back to home using Writeback_M_to_I together with a Writeback_I_Data[Partial] that have the same Transaction ID as the Invalidate_Writeback_M_to_I and hence are part of the same transaction. After the home receives the marker Writeback_M_to_I and commits the data in Writeback_I_Data[Partial] to memory, it finally considers the Invalidate_Writeback_M_to_I transaction to be complete and deallocates the Tracker entry. The Invalidate_Writeback_M_to_I transaction is completed at the IW agent when the Complete response is received from home. The final cache state is Invalid.

Figure 2.16 shows a variant of the previous scenario in which the snoop of Invalidate_Writeback_M_to_I hits a Modified copy at peer caching agent B.

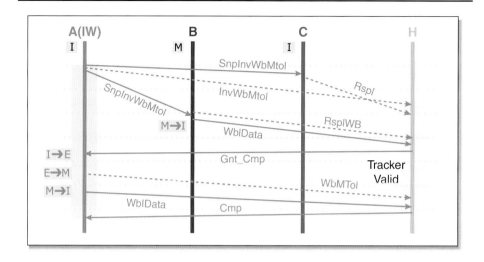

Figure 2.16 Invalidating Write with a HITM

Just like Snoop_Invalidate_I_to_E, this causes the Modified copy at agent B to be written back to home. After the data that is implicitly written back is committed to memory, the home grants exclusive ownership to the IW agent and keeps the Tracker entry of the Invalidate_Writeback_M_to_I transaction active. The rest of the scenario is the same as in Figure 2.15.

The IW agent is allowed to issue Invalidate_Writeback_M_to_I speculatively before it knows for sure whether it actually has any data to write. If it turns out that it has no data to write, then after obtaining exclusive ownership the IW agent just completes the Invalidate_Writeback_M_to_I transaction by issuing Writeback_M_to_I together with a Writeback_I_Data with an empty byte-enable in the latter message.

Using the Home Snoop Behavior

All of the prior examples above used the source snoop behavior, which is designed for low latency at the expense of more snoop traffic in the system. This works well for small systems with up to four or so processors that are likely to be fully connected by Intel QPI links. However, a better choice exists for systems with a large number of processors, or systems where the processors are partially connected and messages may have to be routed over multiple links to reach their final destination. The home snoop behavior is better suited for these systems where link bandwidth is at a premium and the goal is to carefully manage system traffic for the best overall performance. Intel QPI is fully capable of supporting the home snoop behavior for such large systems. A directory or snoop filter can be used in concert with the home snoop behavior to further reduce system traffic and improve system performance. The Intel QPI coherence protocol is very flexible and permits a range of directory or snoop filter schemes to be implemented at the home agent. However, the protocol rules do not define a particular scheme and leave the choice to the implementers of the system. The protocol is designed in such a manner that it requires very little change in the operations of the caching agents in order to accommodate either snoop behavior. The majority of the differences are in the actions of the home agent. The same cache coherence states (Invalid, Shared, Exclusive, Modified) are used in either snoop behavior.

Let us look at examples of typical transactions to coherent memory following the rules of the home snoop behavior. Consider the partially connected four processor system shown in Figure 2.3 for this example. Let us also assume that the each home agents is able to track the state of the caches in a simple directory scheme implemented as part of the memory system. This directory mechanism keeps track of the caching agents that have copies of each cache line and in our example would require four bits of directory state per cache line in the memory.

A Read transaction from a processor checks the local cache for data. Upon a cache miss the request is routed to the protocol layer. A single transaction is issued to the appropriate home agent, requesting the cache line at the particular physical address.

The home agent fetches the data from the specified memory address, using the target address decoder as described before, to address the correct banks of DRAMs in the memory system. The home agent also looks in the directory to determine which of the peer caching agents have copies of the data. The home agent then issues snoops to those agents indicating a Read request. If only one caching agent has the data, it transitions to Shared and sends a snoop response to that effect. If one of the peer caches has the data in the Modified state, it is forwarded to the requester, the local copy is marked as Shared, and a snoop response is sent to the home indicating that data has been forwarded. Upon receiving snoop responses to all the snoops that were issued by the home agent, if none of the peer caching agents has already forwarded data to the requester, then home agent must send the data response to the requester. If no other caches have the data, the data response is sent in the Exclusive state. If one or more caches do have the data, then the data response is returned in the Shared state. The home agent updates its directory and adds the requester to the list of agents that have a copy of the particular cache line.

This snoop behavior, with use of a directory, significantly reduces the number of snoop requests and snoop responses required to complete transactions. However the behavior always incurs the penalty of increased latency because it requires a minimum of three messages for completion. This is the right tradeoff for the large server systems where system bandwidth limits system performance more than latency of each individual transaction.

The Write transaction operates in a similar manner where all the snoops are issued by the home agent. Again the snoops are issued to only those caching agents that have previously fetched that cache line. In this case the home agent issues snoops with a request to invalidate the local copies of data so that the requester can be granted Exclusive ownership. If any one of the caches in the system has a Modified copy of the data, the data response is forwarded directly to the requester in the Modified state, while the state of the line in the sending cache is downgraded to Invalid. This delivers the cache line in the Exclusive state to the requester and the overall transaction has generated far fewer snoops than the source snoop behavior.

The home snoop behavior in Intel QPI is well suited for very large hierarchical systems. Figure 2.17 shows one such system with sixteen processors that are arranged in four nodes of four processors each.

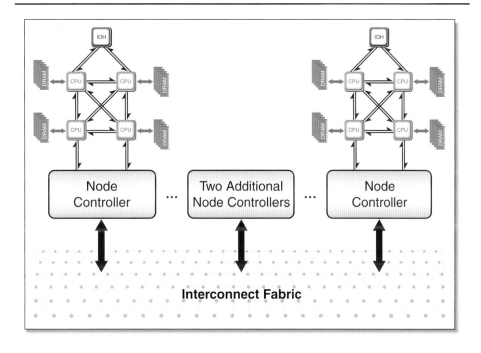

Figure 2.17 Four-Node, Sixteen-Processor system

Each node is composed of four processors and a node controller. The four node controllers are linked to each other over the interconnect fabric, another set of links, essentially creating a hierarchical structure of links. Intel QPI can also be used at the second layer of the hierarchy to tie the node controllers together. Such a system topology is very suitable for construction into rack-based systems. Each of the nodes can be built on a single card that is plugged into a backplane. The backplane carries the links that tie the node controllers together to form the complete system. Such a system architecture has several advantages over a flat system architecture. This system is modular and can be built at a lower cost without compromising system performance. The modularity of the system makes it more scalable, as systems can be built with more nodes to offer increasing levels of performance. The node is also a more readily replaceable unit, helping improve the serviceability of the system. If the node controllers take advantage of the hot-plug capabilities, then the nodes can be replaced without shutting down the whole system.

The home snoop behavior is the better alternative for the system in our example, with sixteen caching agents and an equal number of home agents. Whenever any processor in a node issues a request to the coherent address space, it is either directed at a home agent in the local node, or to the node controller for delivery to a remote home agent. Thus the node controller essentially acts as a surrogate for all the other home agents outside its local node. This makes the node controller an ideal location for a level of directory that would work with the Intel QPI home snoop behavior to manage traffic and latency throughout the system. In this example the directories at the home agents would need to track the status of the local caching agents and just the nodes that have cached data. The node controllers within each node would track the local node's caching agents that contain the particular cache lines. This scheme will help filter traffic at both the levels of the interconnect hierarchy. Snoops will be sent to only those nodes that have cached data, while within the node the node controller will issue snoops to only those caching agents with cached data.

Broadcast Transactions

Some non-coherent requests are required to be broadcast to multiple target entities. In some cases the targets are processor entities and in some cases the targets are I/O entities. For example the Interrupt_Logical and Interrupt_Physical commands are intended for all Interrupt target agents. The Interrupt Target list is a list of Node IDs for agents that are potentially the target of any interrupt. This typically includes processors. Similarly the Interrupt_Priority_Update command is intended for all Interrupt sources. The Interrupt Sources list is a list of Node IDs for agents that are potentially the sources of any interrupt. This typically includes both processors and I/O entities. Figure 2.18 shows the operation of a typical broadcast flow.

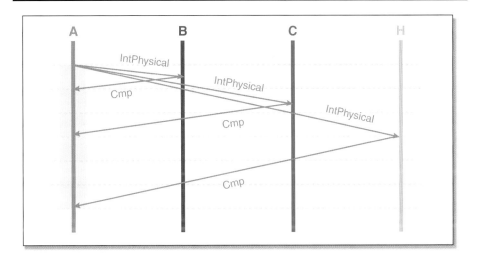

Figure 2.18 Intel® QuickPath Interconnect IntPhysical Broadcast Transaction

In this broadcast transaction from agent A to all the other agents in the system, messages are directed to each agent and resulting in a return of a completion response to the originator. Only after all completions return for each sub-request is the broadcast transaction considered complete. Any order-dependent operation after the broadcast transaction should wait until all sub-completions return to the initiator. If required, each sub-request can be serialized.

If an agent is a target of any broadcast request then it responds with a completion (Cmp or CmpD), without reporting an error condition, to all broadcast requests. This is true even if it is never a target for that particular request transaction. For example, a processor that is a target of some broadcast transaction must respond without error to a broadcast transaction that is specified to target I/O. Note that agents do not need to accept requests that are not broadcast; this would occur on a platform where a broadcast transaction that can be optionally directed, implements the option to direct it.

Broadcast transactions can be used for interrupts, power management, and in some cases cache management. Broadcast transactions are inherently difficult to scale up to large systems with many agents. Intel QPI expects that components implement the broadcast transactions appropriately to accommodate their market requirements. Scaling beyond those capabilities, particularly in hierarchical systems, requires a component to handle the broadcasting beyond the local node of agents. The local node entities broadcast within their local node and this proxy entity is responsible for broadcasting to remote nodes (if required to do so).

Lock Flows

Lock operations in the Intel QuickPath Interconnect are primarily used to support legacy functionality in IA-32 architecture processors. For simplicity, the system lock mechanism supports different types of lock operations using the same transaction flow.

The purpose of locks range from locking one or more addresses for atomic operations to locking the entire Intel QPI network so that no other operations can progress while certain read and write operations issued by the lock agent are in progress. A ProcLock operation is equivalent to the Bus Lock operation on the Intel Pentium 4 bus. The semantics of this lock are that all traffic to a given address, (main memory or memory-mapped I/O space) should be stalled while an atomic read-modify-write operation is processed by the lock agent.

For simplicity, a Processor Lock operation in Intel QPI has stricter semantics in that it locks all traffic from being initiated during the lock with the exception that non-snoopable traffic to DRAM can continue to be issued and completed. Examples of non-snoopable traffic to DRAM include non-snooped AGP accesses and non-snooped PCIe accesses. There should be no latency impact to the types of traffic allowed to proceed during the lock operation.

A ProcSplitLock operation has similar semantics as a Processor Lock except that it is to guarantee atomicity for two read-modify-write operations. Only non-snooped traffic to DRAM is allowed to proceed while the lock is in progress.

A Quiesce operation is a global Intel QPI lock in that all possible traffic that is pending in the fabric *must* be drained and all new traffic must be held off while the Quiesce operation is in progress. In certain configurations where I/O traffic is held off for a lengthy duration, this lock may be destructive, that is, the system is not restartable after the lock sequence.

Lock Transaction Flow

To implement all the above forms of locks with a single transaction flow, different lock types are defined: ProcLock, ProcSplitLock, and Quiesce. The lock flow is initiated with one of these lock requests and terminated with an Unlock message after the atomic update is completed.

The address value in the message specifies either a cache line address or a 4-KB aligned address, depending on implementation. When a cache line address is sent, address bits 11:6 are located in the Byte_Enable fields of the NCM packet type in this case. Quiesce Masters should not depend on the Byte_Enable field being zero in Proc*Lock messages. For Quiesce and UnLock messages, the address value is undefined.

Once the Quiesce Master has accepted a Lock request, the Quiesce Master quiesces the system. The specific traffic that is stalled depends on which lock type was issued. To effect this quiescing operation, stop request messages (StopReq1) are broadcast to the requester's peers and to the requester itself. All targets begin restricting certain types of traffic as specified by the lock qualifier. Once all the completions for the StopReq1 messages are received, StopReq2 messages are broadcast to initiate the second phase of quiescence. When all completion messages for the StopReq2s are received and the Quiesce Master meets the requirements for StopReq2, a completion message to the initiating Lock message is returned to the lock requester. At that point, the lock agent can perform its atomic operations.

The lock requester can perform its atomic operation during the lock phase. Typically the Lock phase consists of a read followed by a write to the same address. In the case of a split-lock, this phase consists of two reads followed by two writes. Since the Quiesce Master is responsible for serializing quiesce and lock flows across the system, Intel QPI agents will never receive other lock requests not affiliated with this flow during the lock phase. However, it is possible that CPU caching agents can receive any other request throughout this phase.

When the atomic operations are completed, the lock requester sends an Unlock message to the Quiesce Master so that all traffic may resume. The Quiesce Master initiates the two-step start request phase to all target lock agents in the partition (or entire domain). When all targets respond with the appropriate completion messages, the Quiesce Master sends a completion message to the lock requester.

If there are other pending ProcLocks in the Quiesce Master, the whole process starts again with the StopReq phases.

Summary

This chapter provided a view into the set of operations that can be performed over the Intel Quickpath Interconnect. These operations are used in systems based on either the IA-32 architecture or the Intel® Itanium® processors. Readers should now have a good understanding of the basic operational flow of transactions in a system based on the Intel QuickPath Interconnect. In the next chapter, we shall look deeper into how the underlying mechanisms work, the ways in which components communicate with each other in order to support the higher level flow of messages.

Chapter 3

Linking Two Devices

Correct me if I'm wrong—the gizmo is connected to the flingflang connected to the watzis, watzis connected to the doo-dad connected to the ding dong.

—Patrick B. Oliphant

This chapter describes the purpose and basic operation of the physical and link layers of the Intel® QuickPath Architecture. These two layers are the foundation for successful high speed communication between two connected devices.

Enabling Communication

In the earlier chapters, we discussed devices that send and receive messages between themselves. These message exchanges accomplish the higher level function needed by the devices that are using the Intel QuickPath Interconnect (Intel QPI). These functions include such things as reading or writing to the main memory space, generating interrupts, or passing configuration information.

In this section we describe the process by which two devices get connected together in order to form a link. Such a link can then be used to communicate the higher level messages between the two devices.

The Problem

The basic problem to be solved at this point is to determine exactly how the two devices will be connected so that they will meet the various constraints imposed by the overall system architecture. In terms of the Intel QPI layers, we will be dealing with the physical and link layers.

Just to refresh the terminology introduced in Chapter 1, two connected link layers communicate with each other at the granularity of a *flit*. In Intel QPI, a flit is always 80 bits of information. The link layer uses the services of the physical layer below it in order to actually get the flits transmitted and received across a physical connection. The unit of information transferred in each unit of time by the physical layer is termed a *phit*. The choice of how wide to make the phit involved a number of factors including cost, performance, and implementation complexity at various widths. The end result for Intel QPI today, is that phits consist of 20, 10, or 5 bits of information for each physical transfer.

Figure 3.1 shows this relationship between two link layers and their corresponding physical layers. The link layer creates flits to be transmitted and the physical layer breaks them up into multiple phits. These phits are then sent one after the other to the receiver. The receiver captures this data and assembles the information back into the flits to pass on to the receiving link layer.

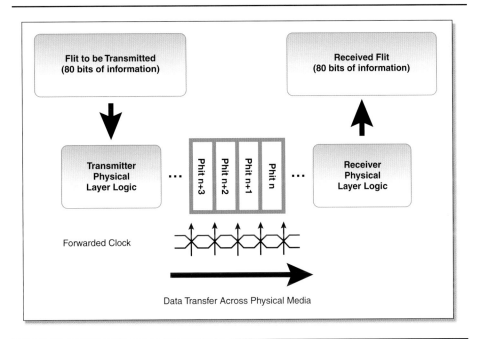

Figure 3.1 Flits and Phits

Goals and Requirements

The Intel QuickPath Interconnect had to satisfy several higher level goals in order to be useful as a high performance system interconnect. These goals included speed, cost, and the ability to use a particular type of connection media.

Speed

One of the primary goals of Intel QPI was to provide a very fast and reliable signaling method between components. This section elaborates on that goal and identifies the previous Front Side Bus (FSB) capabilities that Intel QPI is designed to surpass.

Cost Considerations

Several cost vectors were considered. The actual silicon area needed to implement an Intel QPI port is a key attribute since this interconnect would be used in very high volume, cost-sensitive applications. The number of pins consumed on the device (package costs) is also a key attribute. The cost of the physical interconnect between devices was a constraint since the intent was to stay with the typical PCB manufacturing process that would be used in high volume systems. Finally there were power considerations. Designers had to determine how much of the device's power budget would be allocated to the interconnect.

PCB Traces and Connectors

Primarily driven by cost and manufacturing considerations, the choice was to remain with copper PCB traces. In particular, the initial Intel QPI products were designed to operate over copper traces fabricated on FR-4/epoxy-based printed circuit boards as typically used in high volume system manufacturing. More exotic and costly materials could be used in certain applications in order to offer enhanced performance, but the highest volume products were designed to stay within the constraints of mainstream manufacturing methods.

The electrical signal quality of the interconnect was a design consideration trading off transfer speed, length of interconnect, and number of connectors in the path. In accordance with certain platform design goals, Intel QPI does allow some flexibility in the use of backplane type connectors in the path between the components. Note that this is a product-specific choice and may not apply to all platform types.

Cables and Slots

At this point in the evolution of the Intel QuickPath Interconnect, the usage model is to connect devices either across a single printed circuit board or to allow up to three circuit boards across two connectors. No specific cabling requirements are needed to meet this usage model, but the eventual use of a cable in the connection path is possible within the overall architecture.

In a similar manner, other than the footprint and sockets for the devices that implement Intel QPI ports, no standard mechanical connection point for Intel QPI has yet been defined. PCI Express™ (PCIe™) is available as an industry standard electrical and mechanical interface for I/O devices attaching to a platform. Intel QPI complements these abilities at the platform level and does not replace the role of PCIe.

To summarize, while the engineering development work to facilitate a cabled solution or a standard connection slot has not been done as of this writing, there is no fundamental limitation to creating such solutions.

Electrical Connection—Not Optical or Wireless

Intel QPI is currently designed to connect devices together using today's standard PCB technology with electrical signaling over copper interconnects. Going to optical or wireless interconnects in the future is allowed by the architecture. This would involve creation of a different physical layer than what is used in the current devices.

An Imperfect World

From the start of the definition of the physical and link layers, these layers were intended to be able to cope with a less than perfect interconnect between two devices. In other words, the architects recognized that creating a flawless transmission and reception scheme at the intended signaling speeds would be at the very least prohibitively expensive, if not technically impossible.

High frequency jitter, inter-symbol interference, radio frequency interference (RFI), power supply noise, temperature, and voltage drift are just some of the real world events that can all occasionally combine to result in an information bit being sampled incorrectly. The physical and link layers therefore have been designed to expect and tolerate a very low, but very real, probability of bit errors occurring. This probability is called the Bit Error Rate (BER).

Signaling Tolerates Imperfections

The signaling scheme used across Intel QPI links is not guaranteed to always deliver the bits perfectly across the interconnect. The physical layer has been designed to minimize the probability of incorrect transmission and/or reception of a bit, not down to zero, but down to the specified BER. Techniques built into the interconnect logic used by the devices allow for these routine reception issues to happen, and recovery mechanisms in the link layer are employed so that higher level functions are not affected, or even made aware that these events are occurring.

Devices May Come and Go

Because a system with Intel QPI may be designed to allow for the controlled (no surprises allowed) onlining or offlining of connected devices, the physical layer can contain mechanisms that detect and handle these events. Note that this may not involve the physical addition or removal of a device; powering up or powering down a device and dealing with connection issues is a motivation for including these mechanisms, As we will see later, in-band reset detection is one such mechanism. Another is the existence of a Detect state in the physical layer logical circuits. Together these allow a device to determine if a device at the other end of the link has been added or removed.

Testing the Integrity of the Link

In order to ensure that the link is operating within the specified design limits, the devices themselves have been designed to contain specific capabilities that allow for testing the operation of the link at full speed. These are often referred to as DFX capabilities (DFX = Design For "X" where "X" implies test, debug, or manufacturing).

Purpose of the Physical and Link Layers

The purpose of the physical and link layers is therefore to provide reliable high speed signaling across an imperfect interconnect. We must ensure the higher layers can depend upon this link between two devices, so they can use it to exchange error free messages.

Physical Layer Responsibilities

The basic job of the physical layer is to deliver the 80-bit flits to and from the link layers of two connected devices. At the transmit side, flits are given continuously to the physical layer, which has the task of then delivering them in some manner to the receiving end.

At first glance, we might think that we could just connect 80 wires between two link layers and send the 80-bit flits directly across from one side to the other. A simple parallel clocked interface might suffice. The problem is that such a scheme is not capable of meeting all the goals and requirements as defined in the previous section. Most notably there is no feasible way to use that simplistic type of connection to achieve the intended transfer speeds, which are very fast (and climbing). Interconnect costs in terms of silicon, package, and printed circuit board real estate would also become prohibitive in such a scheme.

Therefore the physical layer, consisting of two sub-blocks of logic and electrical circuitry respectively, was created. The physical layer delivers the link layer's flit information at high speeds across a very challenging interconnect.

Quickly Getting Flits from Point A to Point B

The transfer rates of Intel QPI are driven by the overall performance goals of the platforms that use the interconnect. As processors and intelligent I/O hubs evolve to include additional cores, integrated memory controllers, and sophisticated caching structures, the demands on the interconnect between these devices continue to escalate as well. The first generation products using Intel QPI have transfer rates up to 6.4 gigatransfers per second. This is notated as 6.4 GT/s. Each transfer consists of the amount of information contained in a single phit. For the initial implementations of Intel QPI, the choice was made to use a relatively narrow high speed physical connection where a full-width link is 20 bits (or lanes) wide. Half- or quarter-width operation is also possible as a product-specific optional feature.

Looking at the full width case then shows that each flit will take four transfers (phits) sent across the physical connection. With a 20-bit phit being transferred at the rate of 6.4 GT/s, the average amount of time for each phit is calculated as the inverse of the transfer rate, which yields 156.25 picoseconds (ps) per phit. This is also referred to as the Unit Interval or UI.

The flit rate in this full width case would then be 80 bits being delivered every four UIs. At 6.4 GT/s on the physical connection, this gives a flit rate of 1 flit every 625 picoseconds.

Delivering data reliably at these speeds demands very careful consideration of the transmission effects and the limits on the receiver's ability to recover data successfully. These speeds do not lend themselves to a simple directly connected 80-bit wide parallel interface.

Dealing with an Imperfect Path between A and B

In addition to providing the desired transfer rates, some physical limitations must be dealt with. First, the devices are separated by some distance, which is needed to account for physically placing the devices on the actual printed circuit boards. More complex systems may also partition the logic into multiple boards. Data must be delivered reliably over significant distances. The actual specifications vary from one platform type to another, but a distance of up to 14 inches of copper wiring between two devices, plus up to two connectors in some cases, is a representative example of the platform specifications for the interconnect channel.

In general, signals traveling over longer distances place more severe constraints on the platform. Compressed timing budgets, degraded signal amplitudes, and skew between bit lanes and between the transmitter and receiver clocking are all problems exacerbated by the need to go fast and cover long distances.

The Intel QPI physical layer is designed to provide the features that allow for the fast data rates over longer distances. Furthermore, the burden of meeting these constraints was generally placed upon the driver and receiver circuits in the devices, and not on the need to have extremely tight tolerances in the printed circuit board layout.

For example, the Intel QPI receivers adjust automatically for skew between any individual data lane and the clock path that provides a timing reference (more on this later). This eliminates the need to tightly constrain the PCB routing for all lanes relative to each other and therefore the PCB layout task becomes more straightforward even as the transfer speeds increase. Another example is the use of techniques that pre-shape the transmitted waveforms in order to compensate for signal quality losses that occur as the signal propagates down the interconnect channel. This delivers a usable signal to the receiver without resorting to undue length restrictions or exotic and costly materials for the PCB. Finally, logic in the physical layer can detect the presence or absence of individual bit lanes. This allows bad lanes to be mapped out so that a working link can be established in either the half or quarter width mode.

All of these features combine to make the Intel QPI physical layer a very capable method of delivering information at very high speeds over an imperfect and challenging interconnect environment. Implementing these features in the silicon technology itself, rather than on the external

PCB technology, allows these features to take advantage of the relentless improvements in performance and cost made possible by advances in the silicon technology itself.

Transition from the Intel FSB

For many years, up to and including the timeframe of this writing, the Intel Front Side Bus served as the foundation of multiple processor platforms. Since the FSB is widely used and understood, we will take a look at some features and capabilities of that existing interconnect in order to better understand some of the factors that led to the development of the Intel QuickPath Interconnect. Although it was not specifically architected in a layered fashion, the FSB can be thought of as having a physical layer. The FSB does in fact provide a mechanism for communicating information between at least two connected devices. This section contrasts the approach used in the FSB with the techniques employed in the Intel QPI.

FSB Characteristics

The FSB was designed as a parallel, multi-drop, bus-oriented connection scheme. Early platform configurations allowed up to four processor sockets plus a memory controller chip all connected to the same set of physical wires connecting all the devices. Signaling is bidirectional on the same set of wires and devices arbitrate for ownership of the bus so that only one of the five possible devices is able to transmit at any one point in time.

The data path is a wide parallel bus, with 64 bits (8 bytes) on IA-32 systems and 128 bits (16 bytes) on Intel® Itanium® based systems. Information transfers are accomplished through a source-synchronous strobe signal generated by the transmitter. In this scheme, all information bits are aligned within a close tolerance to that strobe and the receiver circuitry uses that strobe signal to capture the information being sent. While many bus operations take place under control of the common bus clock, information transfers could be quad-pumped, allowing this information to be transferred at a rate four times faster than the common bus clock. For a common bus clock frequency of 400 MHz, this permits information transfers to occur at 1600 megatransfers per second, or 1.6 GT/s. Since each transfer is 8 bytes wide, this gives a transfer rate of 12.8 GB/s (on IA-32 systems).

Figure 3.2 illustrates this timing situation. Two of the actual data signals are shown, along with the strobe signal generated by the transmitter and used by the receiver to capture the data correctly. All data lanes are aligned to the strobe within a skew specification as indicated in the diagram. The alignment of the strobe relative to the valid data window of all the data bits is also a critical timing parameter.

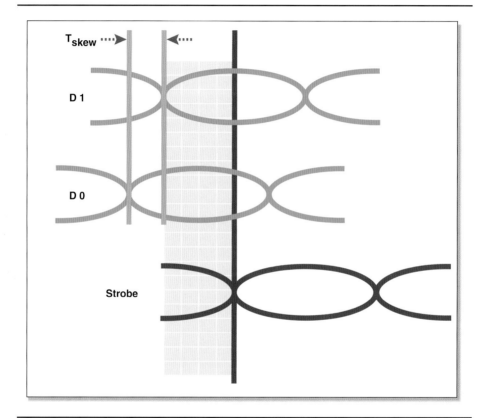

Figure 3.2   Front Side Bus (FSB) Data Strobing

Additional characteristics of the FSB include: Gunning Transistor Logic Plus (GTL+) signaling, separate groups of signals for address, data, and control functions, limited use of parity protection on some elements, and the ability to transfer in only one direction at a time.

While the FSB is a very capable interconnect, some issues came up as the platform requirements evolved, demanding ever higher levels of performance and reliability. One path of the evolution to meet these needs was addressed through the addition of multiple busses. Another path was to increase the common clock rate, and therefore increase the transfer speeds. These techniques work up to a point, but the fundamental nature of the tightly aligned wide data bus with a common strobe signal becomes a very difficult problem to overcome at very high data rates. The timing margins grow increasingly small, and the constraints placed on the PCB designer become ever more stringent.

Platform architects realized that the FSB approach likely would not continue indefinitely to provide all the features and performance demanded by future platform designs, a new approach was called for.

Intel QPI Characteristics

The design of the current Intel QPI physical layer differs significantly from the FSB, and in so doing offers greater performance and a richer feature set. Note that due to its modular approach, different physical layers could be created and still fit within the overall Intel QPI architecture. This modularity allows future growth to be handled in an incremental fashion.

The first fundamental change is the use of unidirectional transfers, using differential signaling. This utilizes a pair of links to connect two components. The pair operating together provides simultaneous bidirectional data transfers. With Intel QPI, there is no need to arbitrate for the right to transmit on a shared bus; each side of the connection has its own dedicated path that can be used continuously. Furthermore, since the connection is point to point, and transfers are unidirectional on a given set of wires, many of the signal quality issues found in a multi-drop bus topology do not exist and therefore the link can more easily operate at much higher data rates. Even so, some signal quality issues, such as discontinuity at a socket or connector and transmission line attenuation effects still exist. Each Intel QPI link is effectively tuned for its own unidirectional path between transmitter and receiver.

A second fundamental change is to move to a relatively narrow interconnect where the information being sent is placed into packets and sent over a multipurpose set of signals. As currently implemented, a full width Intel

QPI link is 20 lanes wide, plus one forwarded clock. All forms of address, control, and data information flow as packets over this single set of shared wires. This narrow interface saves pins on the package, as well as board real estate as compared to the larger set of pins and board real estate utilized by the FSB.

A third fundamental change has to do with how information is transmitted and captured at these high speeds. One part of this change is the use of a common reference clock, which is provided to the two components connected by the link pair. As shown in Figure 3.3, this reference clock is generated by a single frequency source and then is distributed to each component. Each component contains a Phase Locked Loop (PLL) circuit that it uses to generate internal clocking signals. This gives both the receiver and transmitter a shared timing reference that does not vary in frequency from one side of the link to the other. The receiver design capitalizes on this fact as part of the methods it uses to recover data successfully. While this timing reference is part of the solution to recovering data, a more fundamental change is in how the data bits themselves are captured.

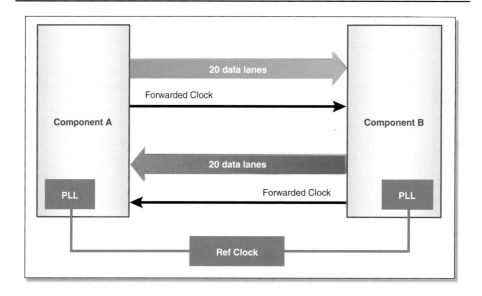

Figure 3.3 Common Reference Clock

The second part of this timing difference from the FSB is also depicted in Figure 3.3. A forwarded clock signal is generated by the transmitter in each component. This forwarded clock is used to help recover the data from the data lanes. This clocking scheme does not rely upon any encoding of a clock embedded within a datastream, it is sent over as an extra signal. While this requires another differential pair on the link, the primary advantage is that no extra transitions are required, as would be the case in an 8b/10b encoding scheme (such as PCIe) where a 10-bit symbol is transmitted to carry 8 bits of useful information. With Intel QPI, each edge of the forwarded clock transfers a phit of information so no bandwidth is lost to clock encoding. This forwarded clock does not directly strobe the data into the receiver, but is used by circuits in the receiver, along with some specialized link training information, in order to create a set of derived clocks (or strobes). See the section on the Physical Layer State Machine later in this chapter for more information on this training process.

Figure 3.4 depicts this timing relationship for these internally derived strobes versus the transmitted data lanes. In the figure, only two of the data lanes are shown, along with the two internally derived clocks for those lanes. Note that the single incoming forwarded clock is used to derive these multiple strobes, one for each lane. The training information allows the receiver to place the strobe point in the middle of the received data window. This is done independently for each lane in order to capture that lane's bits at the optimal point for that lane. Using these multiple internally generated strobes eases the skew requirements for data lanes relative to each other; thereby allowing the speed to be increased without causing undue burden on the PCB routing.

Circuitry in the receiver determines the optimal point to strobe the data. This is done independently for each lane. This removes any short term bit synchronization issues. These very tightly timed internally generated strobes enable much higher data rates than are possible with externally delivered strobes that undergo signal degradation across the physical channel.

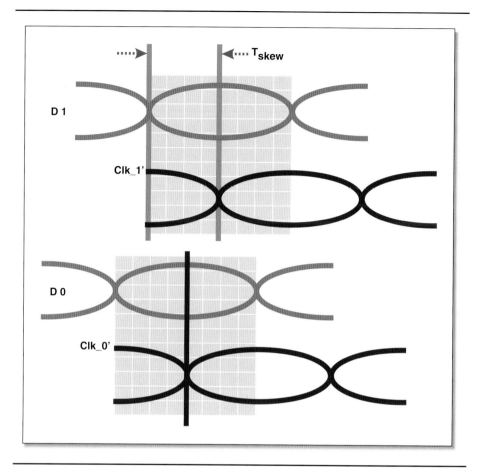

Figure 3.4 Data Strobing Method in Intel® QuickPath Interconnect

To summarize these changes: first, narrow unidirectional links sending packets of information over common wires, second, use of a forwarded clock generating multiple internal strobes to deal with timing issues, and third, differential signaling to help with signal quality concerns at high speeds. Taken together these features provide the physical layer of Intel QPI with the capabilities demanded by the new platform designs.

Logical and Electrical Sub-Blocks

The physical layer takes all the steps needed to establish a connection between two components, and then starts delivering information across that connection. To accomplish that basic task, the physical layer breaks the job down into smaller pieces, starting with the electrical sub-block or module, and then involving the logic sub-block. These modules are depicted in Figure 3.5. Together these two perform the physical layer functions.

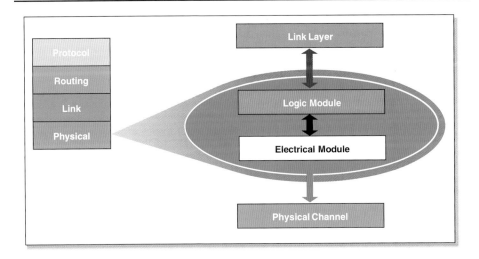

Figure 3.5   Physical Layer Logical and Electrical Sub-Blocks

Physical Layer Electrical Characteristics

This section describes some of the electrical techniques used to provide the high speed transmission paths of Intel QPI. For those readers interested in more specifics regarding the electrical aspects of Intel QPI, please refer to *Mastering High Performance Multiprocessor Signaling: Electrical design with the Intel® QuickPath Interconnect*, by Dave Coleman and Michael Mirmak.

General Features

In terms of the electrical signaling, the current Intel QPI physical layer is a high speed, point-to-point, differential interface. The nominal peak-to-peak differential voltage swing is approximately 1 volt. Signals are referenced to ground; no separate voltage reference level is used at the receiver. Signals are transmitted in a unidirectional manner from the transmitter to the receiver. Information is carried on up to 20 data lanes. There is also one additional clock lane that carries a constant forwarded clock signal running at half the link's transfer rate. For example, if the transfer rate is 6.4 GT/s, the forwarded clock will operate at 3.2 GHz.

When information is transmitted, the basic task of the transmitter is to send all of the data lanes synchronized with a transition of the forwarded clock. Ideally there is close to zero skew between all data lanes introduced at the transmitter side. This is accomplished by careful design of the transmitter circuits and component package. The information is then carried across the interconnect between the devices, which may consist of lengthy traces of copper on the PCB, board layer transitions through vias, and possibly connectors. The interconnect from device to device is referred to as the interconnect *channel*. As the signals flow across this channel, they almost certainly will become distorted in amplitude, pulse shape, and skewed in time relative to each other and the forwarded clock. The combined task of the transmitter and receiver is to overcome these effects and deliver the data successfully.

Transmitter Equalization

Signaling speeds of Intel QPI are now so high, transmission channel artifacts such as frequency dependent attenuation, ringing, and crosstalk will have an influence across several bits of transmitted data. Electrical transitions of the signals result in these effects and their specific characteristics are determined by the interconnect channel between the devices. While proper attention still must be paid to the design and layout of the interconnect, it is not feasible for these ringing and crosstalk effects to be completely eliminated in a system. Rather than place increasingly tight constraints on the design of the interconnect, there is another approach.

One fundamental technique that may be used by Intel QPI devices to overcome issues with delivering data across the channel is the use of *transmitter equalization*. Conceptually, the Intel QPI transmission circuits operate much like a sum-of-products finite impulse response (FIR) type of digital filter. In fact their purpose is to adjust the frequency content of the transmitted signals in order to compensate for frequency related distortion that can occur on the interconnect channel. Once the proper equalization settings have been determined, the circuits work by amplifying or attenuating the drive strength of the transmitter across multiple bits. This mitigates the cumulative effects of ringing or high frequency roll-off. Figure 3.6 gives a conceptual view of this technique. Note that Figure 3.6 illustrates the handling of a single transmitted bit. In fact the circuits operate continuously as the stream of data is sent.

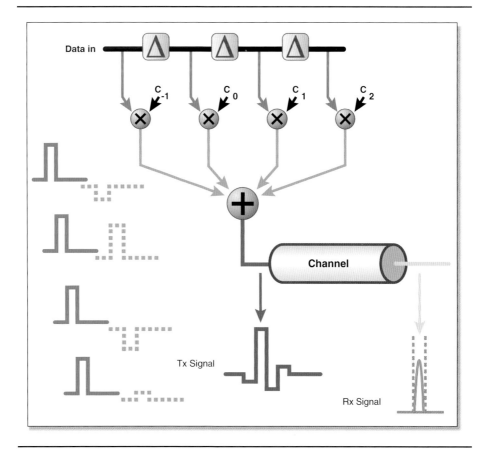

Figure 3.6 Conceptual View of Transmitter Equalization

The basic idea is that the data bit to be transmitted is sent through a series of delay stages that creates a train of pulses, each of which has the same logical value as the bit being transmitted, but which are delayed by one bit time relative to each other. Theses delay stages are indicated by the boxes with the Delta symbols included. The output of these stages is indicated by the four solid line rectangular pulses at the left of the diagram. These stages are often referred to as *taps* and this particular example would be referred to as a four tap equalization circuit.

The next functional blocks are the four multiplication circuits indicated by the circles with the multiplication function shown in the diagram. Each multiplier performs its operation on the incoming data pulse, multiplied by a coefficient value as indicated by the indices C_n. There are four of these as well, indicated by the indices subscripted -1, 0, 1, and 2. Often these are referred to as *tap coefficients*. The output of each multiplier is simply a pulse that has been modified in amplitude as compared to the incoming value. These pulses are indicated by the dashed lines to the left of the diagram.

The output of all the multipliers is then summed, as indicated by the circle with the addition function shown in the diagram, and the resulting waveform is transmitted onto the interconnect channel. This transmitted waveform is shown by the multiple pulse signal at the input to the channel in the diagram.

Again, this represents what happens for just a single bit, represented here as a single 1 in a long string of zeros. When actual data patterns are transmitted, this process goes on continuously at the bit rate of the transmitter. The resulting transmitted waveforms can be quite complex.

This transmitted signal gets distorted in terms of its frequency content and amplitude as it propagates down the channel. The pre-shaping of the transmitted waveform is what counteracts this predictable channel induced distortion so that a relatively clean pulse is delivered to the receiver. The end result is that the receiver will see a pulse from which it can recover the original transmitted data.

The design of the actual transmitter circuits is performed by the product design team and its characteristics are optimized for the characteristics of the general type of channel the product is expected to support. The primary design choices are the number of taps to use, and the accuracy of the math being implemented. The determination of the actual tap coefficients is an analysis task performed by the platform developer. Such analysis is based on models of the transmitter and receiver circuitry, as well as models of the specific interconnect. This combination of component design and the analysis of a platform allows Intel QPI devices to operate properly over relatively long and challenging interconnects.

While the discussion above depicts the circuit as if it were a digital filter, in fact the circuit design is implementing these functions through analog means. The entire process is controlled by digital settings. For example, the actual tap coefficients will be loaded in as some set of fixed precision binary values. The tap coefficient loading process is part of the system initialization process discussed in Chapter 5.

Equalization Example

To illustrate the equalization process in action, some sample data was collected from a test system. The measurement arrangement is shown in Figure 3.7. A processor is driving Intel QPI signals to a *load board* installed in a socket. The load board facilitates the physical probing of the received signals. One received data lane differential pair is probed and measured by the oscilloscope. The forwarded clock is also sampled.

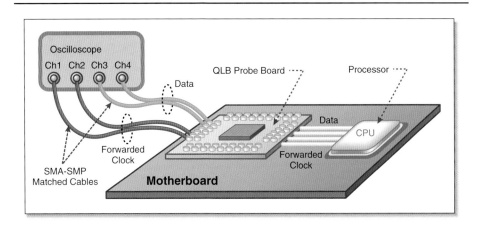

Figure 3.7   Equalization Example Measurement Setup

The first measurement taken will be with no equalization applied. In this case the output drivers are allowed to swing through their entire range. Figure 3.8 shows two things. On the top (a) is the received waveform. The forwarded clock is on the first signal and the second signal is the serial bit stream being sent on that one data lane. Note that the oscilloscope is showing the single-ended signal that has been derived from the difference between the positive and negative sides of the differential pair forming the data lane. On the bottom (b) of Figure 3.8 is the eye diagram that corresponds to the received data lane. Note the degradation of the signals evident both in the oscilloscope display and the eye diagram. In particular there is a large variation in the magnitude of both the high and low signal levels across all the bits. There is also a significant amount of variation in the rise and fall times of the signals. This is evident both in the waveform display and in the non-symmetrical shape of the eye opening. The size of the eye opening, both in the vertical (voltage) and horizontal (timing) dimensions, is reduced to the point that would make it unlikely that data would be received reliably in this case.

The next measurement was taken with the equalization parameters set properly for this particular link on this type of motherboard. Figure 3.9 shows the waveforms captured in this case. Note the very evident improvement in the shape of the received waveform as shown in the waveform display in the top portion of the figure. Most significant is the marked improvement in the size of the eye opening, both in the vertical and horizontal dimensions, shown in the eye diagram view.

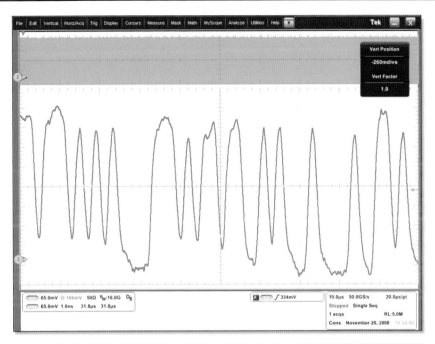

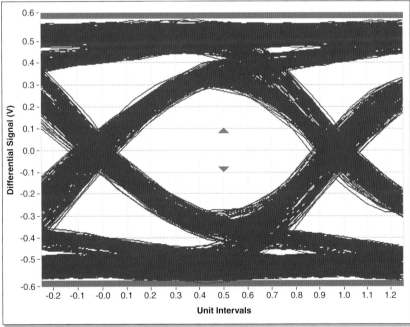

Figure 3.8 No Equalization Applied

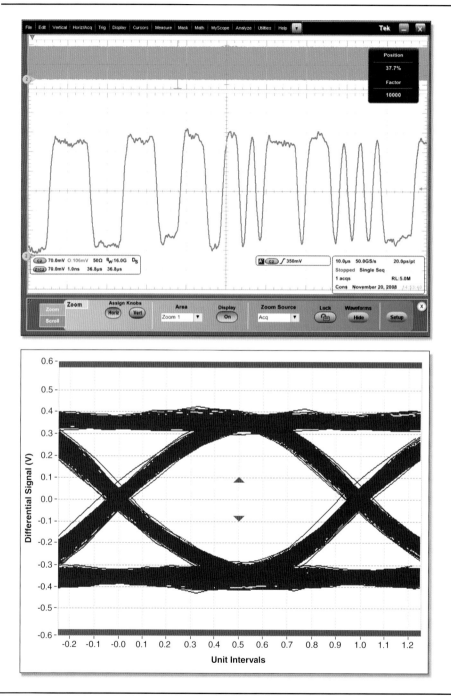

Figure 3.9 Properly Tuned Equalization

Perfection Is Not Required

While the techniques described above help ensure the correct delivery of data, the analysis process is based on statistical methods that allow for a very small probability of the data bit not being received correctly. These methods are beyond the scope of this book. The physical layer's responsibility is to make sure the link operates at a rate better than or equal to the specified BER. The equalization circuits, signaling levels, common reference clock, forwarded clock recovery circuits, and other functions of the physical layer are all part of making sure this takes place. As the final check however, it is a function of the link layer to detect mismatches and take appropriate action. This detection takes place through the use of a Cyclic Redundancy Check (CRC) code, which is used to enable detection of incorrect data flits at the receiver.

Physical Layer Logical Functions

The previous section discussed the operation of the circuits in the Electrical sub-block. This section discusses the functions of the Logic sub-block. At a high level these functions consist of establishing a link, configuring the link according to available resources, and moving to an operational state where flits of information are passed between the connected devices. In addition, providing some test- and diagnostic-related functions is beneficial. All of these functions are driven through finite state machines that react to various events that occur during the initialization and operation of the physical layer.

Basic State Machine

The operation of the physical layer is governed by a finite state machine as shown in Figure 3.10. This diagram shows the basic transitions involved as a device moves from first powering up, until its physical layer reaches the operational state where data is being sent between the two connected devices. The rest of this section discusses the functions performed in these various states.

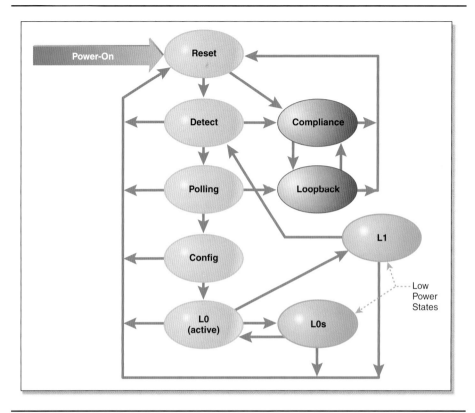

Figure 3.10 Physical Layer Finite State Machine

Reset State

The Reset state is the initial state entered upon power up. Reset is also the final state in the event of a link initialization failure. In this state the device will ensure that various portions of the analog circuitry are calibrated and that device clocking is stable. From that point the state machine will await an internal control signal that indicates it may begin trying to connect to another device.

Finding Another Device (Detect State)

The Detect state is a synchronization point where two devices begin the process of establishing a pair of links between themselves.

The first step is to look for a particular termination resistance to be present, at the receiver's side of the link, on the transmitted signals. If the transmitter's state machine detects the correct termination value, that would indicate the presence of an Intel QPI device at the other end of the link. Another possibility is the detection of a termination that is characteristic of a passive oscilloscope probe. In that case, the state machine proceeds to the Compliance state, which is useful in an offline diagnostic environment. Note that the device will continue looking for one of these two options indefinitely. This facilitates detecting the addition or removal of resources, which is part of the dynamic reconfiguration abilities of Intel QPI.

Once a device is detected, the next step is to look for the forwarded clock from that device. Since this clock is fundamental to data transfer between devices, it must be present before link initialization can proceed further. Both ends of the link perform this function independently, each looking for the clock from the other.

The final step in the Detect state is to look for the presence of working data lanes. Once the clock has been detected and is stable, all receiver lanes on the port are placed into a certain termination state. The transmit side sees that value and responds by driving a known DC (static) pattern on each lane that has detected its receiver. The receiver in turn examines the received pattern. Finding the right value indicates the lane is working. Finding the logical inverse of that pattern tells the receiver that the differential pair has had its positive and negative wires swapped. This is known as *polarity inversion* and is allowed by Intel QPI. PCB layout engineers can use the polarity inversion feature to help simplify the routing of a differential pair of wires; this can help avoid congestion in some cases. Other than connecting the wires either straight through or with polarity inversion, no other action is needed; the receiver simply detects any inversion at this point and adjusts accordingly.

At the exit of the Detect state, we have detected an active Intel QPI device, established the working forwarded clocks, detected the data lanes, and accounted for any polarity inversion. We are now ready to proceed to trying to find actual bits.

Finding Bits and Phits (Polling State)

The first task of the Polling state is to find the correct point at which to capture the bits being sent by each lane of the transmitter. The transmitter sends a particular active pattern on every lane. The receiver then locks onto this incoming bit stream and uses it to fine-tune the bit strobe points established for each lane. Note that this is done independently for each lane. This process cancels out any fine grained skew (less than a bit time) in the incoming data. This continues for a finite amount of time and then the machine proceeds to the next step.

At this point we should be able to capture data from all lanes, but that is not assured. Device or connection failures may prevent the transfer. So the task is to determine exactly which lanes are working, and to cancel out any lane to lane skew that might have been introduced during the transmission across the interconnect channel.

The basic technique used at this point, and in some subsequent states, is to have specific training sequences sent on every lane. The receiver can then detect and examine those sequences in order to find working lanes and to synchronize all the lanes relative to each other. At the end of this process, lanes have either been marked as good or dropped, and all lanes have the same latency as perceived by the receiver's logic. This is how lane to lane skew that exists due to the PCB channel is cancelled out. This eliminates the need to tightly match the PCB trace lengths from one lane to the next.

Exchanging Parameters (Polling State)

At the end of the Polling state, the two sides exchange certain pre-defined parameters that are significant to the operation of the physical layer. Some of this information is used to control the operation of the Loopback state, which is useful for testing the operation of the link at full speed. Other parameters are used to uniquely identify each lane. The receiver examines this incoming information to determine if *lane reversal* exists. Lane reversal is allowed on the PCB connection and is a feature that can be used by the PCB layout engineer to help ease routing congestion in some circumstances. Lane reversal involves the full swapping of the usual straight through connection of the lanes. Normally lane 0 goes to lane 0, lane 1 to lane 1, and so on. With lane reversal, lane 0 would connect to lane 19, lane 1 to lane 18, and so on.

The basic technique used by the physical layer state machine to detect lane reversal is to look for a particular lane number coming in, and then comparing that received lane number to the actual physical lane number at the receiver side. If they match, there is a direct connection. If they mismatch, then lane reversal has been done on the PCB and the receiver can adjust its data multiplexing scheme in order to correctly decode the incoming data.

Note that both polarity inversion and lane reversal are detected automatically by the Intel QPI receiver. There is no need to configure any control registers, or to set any strapping options in the hardware. Any reversal or inversion is simply accounted for in the normal operation of the physical layer state machine. This gives the PCB designer the freedom to choose to use these features if they would be beneficial to simplifying the board layout process.

Establishing the Link Width (Config State)

The Config state is used to negotiate the link width to be used, agree upon certain parameters to be used during normal operation, and to synchronize the boundaries of the flits being sent between the devices.

Recall that in the Polling state, certain lanes may have been marked as dropped. The task at this point is to determine which combination of good lanes will actually be used to form the connection. Intel QPI has defined full-, half-, and quarter-width possibilities. These encompass 20, 10, and 5 lanes respectively. The full 20 lanes can be thought divided into four quadrants, each with five lanes. This is shown in the diagram (a) portion of Figure 3.11 which shows the full flit payload mapped onto the four quadrants labeled Q_0 through Q_3. These quadrants can be combined in various ways to form full-, half-, or quarter-width links. All together there are 11 possible ways: 1 full-, 4 quarter-, and 6 half-width ways that involve various combinations of two quadrants. If any part of a quadrant has a bad lane, the entire quadrant is mapped out.

In the Config state, each transmitter identifies the link width it is capable of using, up to and including all 11 possible combinations. The receiver in turn examines its own capabilities, as well as the indication of bad lanes, and together they come up with the best possible arrangement to use at that time. Referring again to the (a) portion of Figure 3.11, the diagram at the top represents a flit, the fundamental unit of information to be delivered by the physical layer. In this form, all 20 possible lanes are shown, and there are four phits shown. The contents of an 80-bit flit are always 72 bits of Payload (data, address, control, and so on) and 8 bits of CRC code. The task of the physical layer is to deliver this flit over the agreed upon link width.

If all 20 lanes are working, the flit is delivered as shown in the full width flit form at the top of Figure 3.11 (b). There are four physical units (phits) transferred, each of which contains 20 lanes and therefore occupy all four quadrants. If a half-width link is being used, the same flit contents are sent, but this time they are divided up into 8 phits which each contain 10 lanes or two quadrants. The diagram shows this being done using the rightmost two quadrants, but they could be any two working quadrants. Finally, in quarter width, the flit is sent as 16 phits, each with 5 lanes or a single quadrant. Again, the quadrant chosen could be any of the four, not limited to just the example shown. The mapping of the flit contents onto the available quadrants for full- half- and quarter-width links is shown in Figure 3.11 (b).

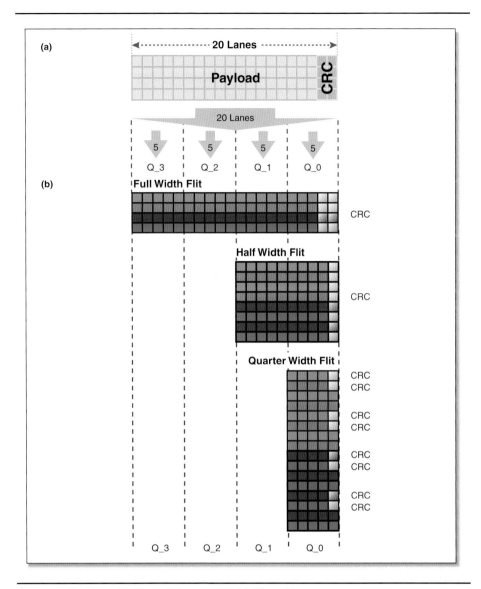

Figure 3.11 Full-, Half-, and Quarter-Width Transfers

In all reduced width cases the same flit information is transferred across the physical layer; no functionality (including error protection) is lost. The only difference is in performance. It takes two or four times as long to transfer the flit. Other than possibly taking note of that fact, the upper layers are not even aware of the width of the link being used. The intent of this feature is twofold. One is to provide a degree of fault tolerance. The link can be established even in the presence of multiple hard failures on the lanes. The second is to allow products to choose to implement lower width ports, which trades off some performance for savings in terms of interconnect costs. The choice of which link widths to support is a product-specific choice made in order to meet the performance, cost, and availability constraints for a particular platform.

Parameters and Flit Lock (Config State)

The final steps in the Config state have to do with negotiating parameters that will be used for certain operations during the normal link operation. These are primarily counters that are used by the physical layer to determine the periodicity and duration of a "retraining" operation. This is used on a periodic basis to re-establish bit synchronization at the receiver. Both sides of the link are expected to enter and exit this retraining period at the same time and it is this parameter exchange that establishes the specific time values to be used.

At this point the only remaining step is to establish the boundaries of the actual flits and move into the operational state. Upon the receipt of a control signal generated within a device, the transmitter will transition from sending the Training Sequences that have been used up until this point, to the sending of actual flits. A handshake process ensures that the transmitter and receiver for each link do this at the correct point. Note that the link in each direction would typically do this at different times. Once this has been completed, the link pair is in the operational state.

Transition to Operational State L0

At this point the physical layer is now initialized and sending whatever flits are given to it by the link layer. These flits contain the messages or null traffic being communicated between the two agents. The link is always transmitting something, so if the agent has no real information to send, a null packet is sent instead. From the physical layer's perspective, all flits are sent across, but the physical layer does not care about the actual contents of those flits. All flits, including nulls, are supplied by the link layer, and are simply delivered by the physical layer. Other than that ongoing process, there are a few points worth noting about routine events that can and do take place in the L0 normal operational state.

Data Scrambling

Once in the L0 state, all flits are put through a data scrambling circuit before transmission on the link. The receiver performs a complementary descrambling operation to recover the original data. This process helps improve the timing characteristics of data recovery. From a signal integrity perspective, certain data patterns may induce stress on the signal, either in terms of crosstalk or inter-symbol interference. The use of data scrambling techniques has the benefit that any given data pattern from a transmitter will not be generated repeatedly over a link. Data scrambling helps reduce inter-symbol interference and also helps ensure that the average signal is evenly biased between the high and low values. This technique helps in managing the BER of the link and with device power distribution issues.

Periodic Retraining

Retraining is the process of reestablishing the fine grained bit synchronization as originally performed in the Polling state. At a specified periodic interval, and for a specified duration, the link suspends transmission of flits and sends the retraining pattern. While the exact values used are platform-specific and may vary, generally the interval is on the order of tens of milliseconds and the duration would be around 2000 UI (bit times). This retraining helps prevent long term drift in the strobing of incoming bits and therefore helps the link maintain the specified BER over time. Such drift may be due to relatively slow long term changes such as temperature or voltage related effects on the components at either end of the link.

Link Power Management States - L0s and L1

In the L0 state, all data lanes and the forwarded clock are operating continuously. The L0 state provides maximum throughput to the higher layers that are using the link. In the L0 state however, the link also consumes the greatest amount of power. In order to provide ways of managing the power consumption, two link low power states have been defined, L0s and L1.

In the L0s state, all of the data lanes except for one are turned off completely. The one remaining lane is held in a static differential state. This sense lane is used to signal the transition back to normal operation. In L0s, the forwarded clock keeps running, so both sides of the link can stay in sync down to the bit time level. The L0s state saves power as compared to the L0 state and also provides a fast transition back to L0 when normal data flow resumes.

In the L1 state, the greatest power savings can be achieved because all of the data lanes and the forwarded clock can be turned off. The L1 state also allows circuitry within the transmitter's and receiver's physical layers to be powered down as well. The L1 state achieves greater power savings than the L0s state, but the tradeoff is that the link takes longer to get back to normal operation. In fact the physical layer generally would go back through most of the full state machine process in order to reestablish the connection.

These three states are depicted in Figure 3.12. The maximum performance mode is L0 on the left, maximum power savings is L1 on the right.

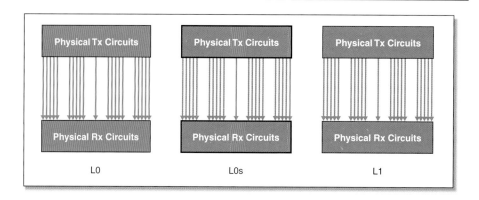

Figure 3.12 Link Normal and Low Power States

Physical Layer Miscellaneous Topics

The next few sections discuss some topics related to the operation or maintenance aspects of the physical layer. The topics covered include how a reset message is communicated between the components and also how the operational speed of the link is established.

Taking Down a Link—Inband Reset

Inband Reset is a mechanism where a receiving physical layer can detect that the device at the transmitting end has dropped off the link for some reason. With two connected devices, each device will monitor the incoming link. The Inband Reset event takes the physical layer back to the Reset state in the state machine where it will follow the process to try and re-establish the connection. Inband Reset is detected by the stopping of the forwarded clock. This is termed an Inband Reset because it does not make use of any "sideband" signals, it is performed using the signals that exist on the interconnect and that are used for normal operation.

Inband Reset events are useful for facilitating resource addition and removal. They are also used as part of the recovery scheme for recovering from persistent bit errors that might have occurred on the link.

Inband Reset affects only the physical layer. Higher layers are not necessarily affected by this event assuming the link can be re-established after the reset.

Link Speed

The speed at which a link operates is determined by control register settings within the device. In the current product examples, no auto-configuration is performed by the link itself to attempt to determine what speed will be used. Since both ends of the link must be operating at the same speed, it is vital that the registers in both devices be set appropriately.

In order to facilitate initial system startup where the characteristics of the device and the interconnect channel may not be known, the current Intel QPI physical layer defines a default slow mode speed. This allows devices to power on and start communicating with no modifications to register settings performed before operations begin. This slow mode is currently defined as one fourth the rate of the reference clock input. For example, if the reference clock input is 133.333 MHz, the slow mode would result in a forwarded clock rate of 33.333 MHz which yields a transfer rate on the link of 66.66 MT/s. At these speeds the signal quality degradation is greatly reduced and there is considerably more timing margin to work with. This allows the two devices to establish a connection. Once established, system firmware can begin execution (more on this in the next chapter) and the firmware can program the devices for full speed operation.

Core Speed and Link Speed

In contrast to systems that used the FSB, the operational speed of the CPU core and the operational speed of the system interconnect are not coupled together through some sort of bus ratio multiplier. In Intel QPI systems, the CPU clock rate and the link speeds can be controlled independently. Some product-specific restrictions may apply, but as a general rule the two rates are not tied to each other. This allows considerable freedom in pushing up the performance of either the CPU or the interconnect without having to be concerned about one affecting the other.

Link Layer Responsibilities

Once the physical layer has established a connection and progressed up to the operational L0 state, it will be continuously delivering flits of data across that connection. At that point the physical layer has basically completed its task, other than as noted in the earlier section regarding retraining and low power states. The actual information content of the flits being sent and received is of no interest to the physical layer.

The next step is for the two link layers to get logically connected and establish a way of using the physical connection in order to pass meaningful messages between the components in a controlled and reliable manner. This is where the link layer functions begin. The link layer (once initialized) provides three basic functions.

1. Higher layer services

2. Flow control

3. Error detection and recovery

Higher Layer Services

Due to the modular nature of the overall Intel QPI layered architecture, from the perspective of the higher layers the physical layer is invisible. All of the details of how the connection actually takes place are not important to the higher levels. The link layer is aware of certain events and characteristics of the physical layer, but it abstracts away those details in terms of the services it provides to the higher layers. Those services allow the link layer to make it appear as if there were multiple virtual channels between the two connected devices, rather than the single physical set of wires. Through the use of message classes and virtual networks as implemented by the link layer, it is able to provide multiple independent transmission channels to the higher layers in the architecture. Those higher layers rely upon that independence in order to ensure the protocols operate correctly without a deadlock situation occurring.

Flow Control

Flow control involves the controlled sending of information between the transmitter and receiver so that system resources are not overwhelmed by the traffic. Intel QPI uses a credit/debit scheme to control the flow of flits and/or packets between the devices. Based on the design and configuration of its logic, the receiving device is capable of handling a finite amount of information at any one time. The receiver grants the transmitter permission to send information into that finite resource by granting "credits" to the transmitter. The transmitter must possess a credit before it can send that information. Once it does send, it decrements (debits) the available count. Once the receiver has consumed the information and released the buffer resources, it will again grant a credit back to the transmitter. Credit information is encoded as part of the packet format and can therefore be returned along with normal data flow process. If no message needs to be sent, an Idle packet can be used to return credit information. This process goes on continuously during link operation. In order to preserve the independence of the virtual connections, there are multiple independent credit pools that are managed by the link layer.

Error Detection and Recovery

While the physical layer does not care about the overall data content being sent, other than meeting the specified BER, the link layer most certainly does care. It is the function of the link layer to provide for detecting errors in the transmitted data, recovering from those errors, and making sure that only the good flits and packets are passed up to the higher layers. Error detection is accomplished though the use of a CRC code embedded within every flit. The transmitter's link layer generates this code and the receiver checks the entire received flit including the CRC code to determine if the flit was received correctly. If an error is detected, a "Back-up-N" and retransmit scheme is invoked in order to recover the correct information.

Details of Link Layer Functions

The link layer contains several related but somewhat independent functions. It begins with an initialization state machine. Parameters are exchanged as part of this initialization and those parameters influence how the link layer operates. Once initialized, the link layer performs its three basic responsibilities as defined in the preceding section. In addition, once the physical layer reaches the L0 state, the link layer is responsible for providing all flits that are to be transmitted. If there is no actual traffic to be sent, a special flit called a Null flit is sent instead.

The following sections describe how the link layer performs these functions.

Link Layer Initialization

Link layer initialization takes place after any device reset, whenever certain device control register bits are changed, and whenever a specific Ready_For_Init flit is received from the device at the other end of the link. In contrast to the physical layer, more care must be taken prior to performing a link layer initialization because state information pertinent to managing the information content of the higher layers could be lost if the initialization is performed indiscriminately.

Ready for Initialization

To perform the initialization, the link layer first waits for the physical layer to establish the connection and get to the L0 state. At this point the link layer is providing all flit content and it begins by sending Ready_For_Init flits. Each side must be sending and receiving the Ready_For_Init flit in order for an interlock to be achieved. Once interlock is achieved, the link layers can move on to the parameter exchange phase of link initialization.

Parameter Exchange and Feature Selection

In this phase, the two link layers send a series of flits containing parameters that are pertinent to the operation of the link layer. These parameters include: size of the retry buffer, port number of the sender, NodeID information, CRC mode supported, ability to support low power states, and bits that identify the type of agent sending the information. The receiving link layer captures this information into status and control registers. The device hardware may take direct action based on these parameters, but more typically it is a function of the platform configuration firmware to examine these captured values and configure various capabilities accordingly. In the next chapter we show how overall system initialization proceeds based upon the type of information captured during this low level parameter exchange.

Ready for Normal Operation

We have now reached the second interlock point of the link layer initialization process. Once the device has completed sending and capturing the parameters, it can configure itself as needed and then move on to sending a Ready_For_Normal_Operation flit. Once a device is both sending and receiving the Ready_For_Normal_Operation flit, the second interlock has been reached and the link layer can then commence sending and receiving normal traffic.

Services to Higher Layers

Everything in the physical and link layer up until this point has been involved with preparing the hardware of the two connected devices to be able to communicate. Now that this point has been reached, it is time to start sending real messages. So what are real messages and how are they handled?

At a basic level, two types of messages are handled by the link layer. The first is the traffic that consists of requests and responses between logical agents. Examples of such communication were covered in Chapter 2. The second basic type consists of link layer specific messages used to help manage the overall connection. Examples of this type are messages used for link initialization, flow control, error handling events, and link idle conditions. The link layer segregates and manages all this traffic by using the techniques of multiple message classes and multiple virtual networks.

Message Classes

Having multiple message classes defined provides independent transmission channels to the Protocol layer agents. Some of the aspects of correct protocol operation rely upon the assurance that the link layer will create no dependencies between the traffic in one message class and the traffic in any other message class. Stated another way, temporary blockages in one message class must not prevent traffic from flowing in other message classes.

Six message classes are currently defined as shown in Table 3.1. One special message class is also shown. The messages with the SNP, NDR, DRS, NCS and NCB message encodings are unordered. An unordered channel has no required relationship between the order in which messages are sent on that channel and the order in which they are received. The HOM message class does have some limited ordering requirements to which components are designed to comply.

Table 3.1   Message Classes

Message Class	Abbreviation	Ordering Requirements	Data Content?
Snoop	SNP	None	No
Home	HOM	Limited	No
Data Response	DRS	None	Yes
Non-Data Response	NDR	None	No
Non-coherent Standard	NCS	None	No1
Non-coherent Bypass	NCB	None	Yes
Special (Link Management)	SPC	None	No

1   See section on NCS for more information

Snoop Message Class—SNP

The SNP class is for messages that are initiated by an agent that wishes to determine the coherence state of a particular cache line within the cache structure of the agent being snooped. These may be initiated by the caching agent generating the request (source snoop behavior) or by the home agent responsible for the cache line (home snoop behavior), but the target of a snoop message is always a caching agent. The size of a SNP message is the minimum packet size, which is either one or two flits depending on the packet type supported by the platform. More on how packets are formed later in this chapter.

Home Message Class—HOM

HOM class traffic consists of requests for access to the coherent data space, or for snoop responses related to those requests and to the SNP messages. HOM traffic is always directed to the home agent responsible for that particular address in the coherent memory space. Requests are always generated by a caching agent. Snoop responses are also always generated by the caching agent. HOM messages are also the minimum packet size of 1 or 2 flits.

   In current products, the ordering requirement placed upon HOM messages is as follows. For any given caching agent (source) and home agent (destination) combination, messages are kept in order on a per-address basis. Messages from different sources or being sent to different destinations have no ordering requirements respective to each other. Likewise messages to different addresses have no ordering requirements relative to each other. Current home agent designs rely upon the link layer maintaining this HOM channel ordering to ensure proper operation of the coherent protocol.

Data Response—DRS

DRS messages contain the actual data to be returned in response to a request on the HOM channel. The data response may come from the home agent responsible for that line of main coherent memory, or it may come from another caching agent in the system. The DRS message is directed to the caching agent that issued the original request on the HOM channel. Full cache line transfers can be performed using the DRS channel; this delivers up to 64 bytes of data. The packet size is therefore larger, consisting of the header flit(s) plus eight data flits. Partial line sizes are also supported.

Non-Data Response—NDR

NDR messages are control messages sent to the caching agents, either to indicate the completion of a transaction or to force the caching agent to take additional actions involved with the resolution of some aspect of the cache line's ownership. As the name implies the NDR messages contain no actual data and therefore the minimum packet size of 1 or 2 flits can be used.

Non-Coherent Standard—NCS

NCS messages are requests dealing with access to system resources that are generally outside of the coherent memory space. This includes things such as reads to non-coherent memory regions, read and write configuration and I/O space transactions, and interrupt acknowledgements. Certain NCS transactions can also access the coherent memory space, but it is not required that coherency be maintained by the Intel QPI hardware in this case. Such read requests would be performed without the addition of snoop requests and responses. Small packets are used, ranging from the minimum packet size, up to three flit packet sizes for some message types. NCS packets do not contain any data flits. However, some messages in NCS support up to an 8 byte payload embedded into the packet's header flits.

Non-Coherent Bypass—NCB

NCB messages are where we find the write transactions to the non-coherent memory regions. Interrupt requests and other control type messages are also part of the NCB class. Similar to the NCS traffic, no coherency messages are generated in response to these write transactions. It is the responsibility of the overall system configuration as well as software policies to ensure that any desired data consistency is maintained for system resources being accessed with these messages. NCB messages are targeted to several possible destinations such as a non-coherent memory space, a processor for interrupts, or an I/O controller for peer-to-peer I/O traffic. These messages carry data fields up to and including a full 64 bytes. Therefore the packets sizes are large, up to eleven flits in some cases.

Special Messages—SPC

Messages in the SPC class are used for link traffic management, and they do not involve the higher level Protocol layer agents. These messages are how the two connected link layers communicate with each other. These link-to-link control messages are used for error correction (link level retry), power management, system configuration, initialization, debug, and for sending Idle or null flits during periods when there is no actual Protocol layer traffic to send. The link initialization and parameter exchange process described earlier in this chapter is an example of one use of SPC messages. Packet size is a single flit. Note also that SPC packets do not utilize the same flow control management as the other message classes. In particular they do not make use of credits before they can be transmitted.

Virtual Networks

Virtual networks provide an additional method at the link layer to enable replicating each message class into independent virtual channels. The link layer supports up to three virtual networks. Each message class is subdivided among the three virtual networks. There are up to two independently buffered virtual networks (identified as VN0 and VN1) and one shared adaptive buffered virtual network (termed VNA).

Figure 3.13 illustrates this process of mapping transactions coming from the Protocol layer into the appropriate message class, and then further subdividing the traffic by selecting one of the available virtual networks. It is the combination of a message class and a virtual network that results in what is called a virtual channel. The total number of virtual channels supported by the link layer is therefore the product of the number of virtual networks supported and the number of message classes supported. For Intel QPI, this is a maximum of eighteen virtual channels (three SNP, three HOM, three NDR, three DRS, three NCS, and three NCB). This provides up to 18 unique ways to manage the traffic flowing onto the single physical connection.

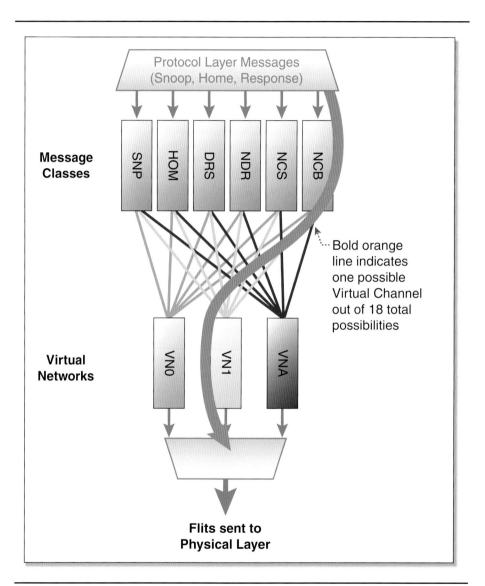

Figure 3.13 Message Classes, Virtual Networks, and Virtual Channels

Flow Control

The link layer implements a credit/debit based flow control scheme in which the sending link layer must possess a *credit* for the piece of information that it wishes to send. That credit ensures that the receiver is capable of receiving the entire packet or flit. Intel QPI does not allow a receiver to ignore a transmitted piece of information. So, to allow the flow of information to be regulated, the receiver controls the granting of these credits. The number of credits to be issued is determined by the receiver since it knows how many physical buffers it has available.

Credit Management

Figure 3.14 illustrates this credit and debit process. On the receiver side (Rx) a certain number of buffers are available. This is determined by the design of the Rx hardware. The Rx side grants credits to the transmitter (Tx) side. Each credit ensures that the Rx can accept one buffer slot worth of information. The Tx side can accumulate multiple credits if it does not have anything to transmit at that moment. It must possess a credit however in order to be able to send a message. Once sent, the Tx side decrements or debits its count of available credits. If the count reaches zero it cannot transmit. The Rx side consumes the messages from its incoming buffer space and once the buffer is free it can once again grant a credit back to the Tx side. This process of granting credits from the Rx side, and incrementing or decrementing the available credit count goes on continuously during normal traffic flow between the two link layers.

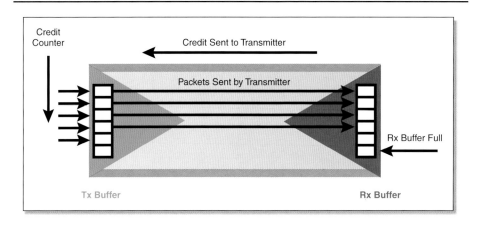

Figure 3.14 Buffers and Credit Management

Credit Pools

Because the link layer must keep the traffic on the individual message classes independent from each other, the link layer is designed to ensure that these buffer resources and the credits used to manage them are also managed properly. It does this through the use of properly designed buffer spaces and independent credit pools.

For the VN0 and VN1 virtual networks, each message class is buffered independently on a packet size basis. A credit granted in this case indicates the Rx side can accept anything up to and including a full packet. Remember that this could include multiple flits in many cases. Each message class in VN0 and VN1 therefore has its own credit pool to manage traffic to those buffers. A link layer that implements both VN0 and VN1 would therefore manage twelve credit pools based on the six message classes and the two virtual networks. The number of credits available in each message class is specific to each unique device. It must be a minimum of one packet per message class, but could be larger.

Multiple Virtual Networks and Credit Pools

The use of dedicated packet sized buffer space used by VN0 and VN1 could become expensive in terms of the amount of actual silicon resources needed to implement those buffers. Furthermore, the utilization of those buffers may be less than optimal because actual interconnect traffic patterns will be dynamically shifting. The VNA virtual network was created to address this issue.

In VNA there is a single pool of buffers, sized as a single flit each, all managed by a single credit pool. Traffic from all message classes can share these buffers as long as the link layer maintains the required independency. This allows the hardware resource (buffer space) to be more effectively used during normal message flow on the link. The size of the credit pool for VNA is again a device specific parameter but a typical size would be on the order of 100 flits.

If a device implements VNA, it will also implement at least VN0 in order to provide a way to break out of possible traffic deadlock scenarios.

Link Reliability

As discussed in the section on the physical layer, the interconnect between two devices is not expected to be perfect. The physical layer will maintain proper data transmission and reception of the bits flowing across the link, but there is a very small but finite probability that any individual bit will not be received correctly. In order to deal with these routine events, the link layer has been designed to detect and correct for their occurrence. This is accomplished through the use of a CRC code for error detection, and a retry mechanism for recovery. Together these provide a very robust way to accomplish proper communication at the high bit rates used over the physical connection.

Transmitter Tasks

At the transmitter, the link layer is forming flits to be sent across to the other side. Recall Figure 3.11 where the basic format of a flit was shown, with 72 bits of payload, plus 8 bits of CRC code. The link layer computes this 8 bit code for every outgoing flit, including Idle and Null flits, and embeds that code within the flit itself.

The other task at the transmitter side is to save the outgoing flits into a retry buffer. This allows them to be recalled in case they are needed to recover from any error detected by the CRC checking. Most but not all flits are placed in the retry buffer. Null flits in particular are not since they convey no information at all and are just used as filler during idle periods on the link. Idle flits do enter the retry buffer since they are used to convey some information, notably the return of credit information. As flits are placed in the Retry buffer, the transmitter keeps track of them through the use of pointers to that information.

Standard CRC Protection

Cyclic redundancy checks (CRCs) are a widely used type of error detecting code. As mentioned earlier, the link layer uses an eight-bit CRC (commonly referred to as CRC8) to protect the link from transmission errors. The transmitter computes and appends the CRC to every flit. The CRC polynomial chosen for Intel QPI is $x^8 + x^7 + x^2 + 1$. This specific CRC8 has the following characteristics:

- All 1b, 2b, and 3b errors are detected.
- Any odd number of bit errors is detected.
- All bit errors of "burst length" 8 or less are detected. Burst length refers to the number of contiguous bits in error in the payload being checked.
- 99 percent of all errors of burst length 9 are detected.
- 99.6 percent of all errors of burst length greater than 9 are detected.

The choice of this particular CRC8 calculation has made the assumption that bit errors are more prone to happen down (in time) a particular lane as opposed to across multiple bits in a phit.

Rolling CRC Protection

For some demanding applications the standard CRC8 is not sufficient protection over a flit on a link. An example would be a physical layer that supports width reduction to quarter width. For those cases, Intel QPI has provided an optional link protection mechanism. As opposed to making a larger CRC polynomial, which would have changed the flit encoding, Intel

QPI developed a methodology to increase coverage without growing the CRC polynomial. This increased coverage methodology is referred to as *rolling CRC*. This methodology allows the flit format (80-bit definition of 72 bits payload + 8 bits CRC) to stay exactly the same between the normal CRC and the rolling CRC algorithm.

Rolling CRC simply incorporates the calculated CRC value for the previous flit into the calculation of the current flit. This method of rolling CRC, while only consuming 8 bits of the 80-bit flit, provides similar coverage to a 16-bit CRC code (CRC16). The rolling CRC mechanism provides all the capabilities of the CRC8, as well as the capability to detect all burst errors of length 15 or less and most burst errors of length 16. Figures 3.15 and 3.16 show in more detail the generation and checking of rolling CRC. GA represents the CRC8 polynomial of $x^8 + x^7 + x^2 +1$, while GB represents the additional polynomial of $x^8 + x^7 + x^3 + x^2 +1$ that is introduced in this mode.

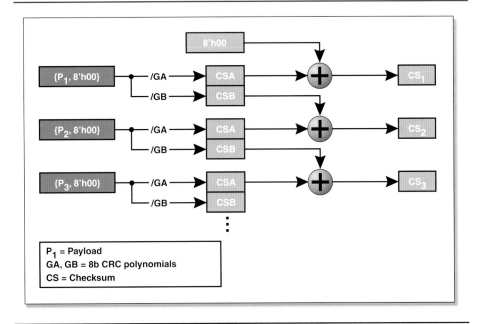

Figure 3.15 Rolling CRC Generation Scheme

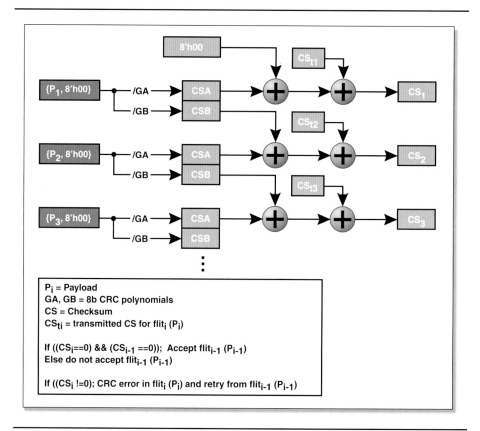

Figure 3.16 Checking Incoming Rolling CRC

Due to the optional nature of this feature, the link layers negotiate the proper CRC mode, based on hardware support, during the initial Parameter Exchange state machine of the link layer. Parameter Exchange is performed in the base CRC8 mode, and information is exchanged related to the supported transmit and receive capabilities of both components. The least common denominator of the two is then chosen for each direction of the link. Due to this, it is possible to have one direction of the link pair running in CRC8 mode, while the other direction is running in rolling CRC mode.

Receiver Tasks

At the receiver, the entire content of the flit, including the CRC code, is run through a checking process. The end result indicates whether the received flit is entirely good or if it contains any errors due to transmission issues.

If the flit is good, the receiver passes the information on to the next higher level in the architecture. Once this is done the receiver can return a credit if the buffer space is freed up. The other step is to periodically acknowledge (Ack) proper reception of the flits so that the transmitter can remove them from its retry buffer. This Ack process takes place every 8 flits. Ack and credit information is returned embedded in messages heading back to the other side of the link where that transmitter can adjust its credit and retry buffer pointers accordingly.

If the flit is not good, as indicated by an incorrect result in the CRC calculation, the receiver discards the incoming flit and enters into a recovery process known as link level retry (LLR). The LLR flow starts with the sending of an LLR Request SPC packet from the receiver back to the transmitter. This request also includes a pointer that informs the transmitter how far back in its retry buffer it needs to go. The two sides then proceed through the process of backing up the transmitter, resending flits from the specified point, and rechecking the incoming flits for correct CRC results. If they are correct, the normal flow of flits resumes along with the return of Ack and credit information.

Link Layer Retry

As stated earlier, it is expected that there will be occasional bit flips that can corrupt a request (possibly an address bit), snoop response, or an actual data bit. All of these are potential forms of data corruption that are dealt with by the link hardware, and the CRC algorithms described previously do an excellent job of detecting and signaling that an error has occurred. These CRC algorithms do not, however, correct the error itself. The Intel QuickPath Architecture, like PCIe, places the burden of the link recovery in the link layer and employs a link layer retry mechanism as the means to survive these routine random transmission errors.

The retry mechanism relies on a link level retry buffer, which maintains copies of all sent flits at the transmitter until the receiver has indicated error-free reception of the flits. These are implemented as circular buffers, with a write pointer that wraps around to zero when it reaches the end. The location of flits in these retry buffers is managed by both the transmitter and receiver on the link, using the concept of a sequence number. The sequence numbers are set to a value of zero at reset time, and tracked using a wrapping counter as flits are transmitted or received. The wrap values for the buffers are exchanged before link layer traffic is active during Link Layer Parameter Exchange. From this point forward, the exchange of sequence numbers occurs only through link level retry messages during the link level retry sequence triggered by a detected error. Tail pointers, which track the position of the oldest flit in the buffer, advance when acknowledgements (or Acks) from the receiver indicate that flits have been received error free. This advancement of the tail pointer effectively deallocates flits from the buffer.

For performance reasons, the link level retry buffer (located in each transmitter) is sized to take into account the roundtrip delay of the link. This is because the transmitter should stop sending flits if the retry buffer ever fills. In short, to utilize the entire available bandwidth of the link, the link layer retry buffer should be sized for the round-trip delay. It must take into consideration

- The sending of a flit from the sender link layer through its physical layer.

- The flight time of the packet from sender through receiver physical layer.

- The process time to detect an error in a flit at the receiver link layer.

- The time to send an error indication from receiver back to the sender.

- The flight time of the error indication from the receiver to the sender.

- The processing of the error indication at the original sender.

- The number of flits being acknowledged per an ack from the receiver (for intel QPI, the number of Protocol level and link layer flits carrying credit information being acknowledged by each Ack is eight).

The link layer retry mechanism is functionally split between the two ends of the link. There are state machines at both ends of the link in each direction. The state machines are referred to as the Remote Retry State Machine (RRSM) and the Local Retry State Machine (LRSM). The RRSM is located in the receiver and the LRSM is located in the transmitter. These state machines control the sequencing of the retry protocol, the use of the retry buffer, and the tracking of the sequence number.

In addition, the LRSM in the transmitter contains the following pieces

■ Link Layer Retry Buffer – the size of the buffer is product-specific, but the size is revealed during link initialization. It is implemented as a circular buffer.

■ Three Pointers

– Tail Pointer – separates available entries and used entries.

– Write Pointer – Points at the next location to be written in the retry buffer for transmitted flits.

– Read Pointer - In the case of a CRC error and a request for retransmission, the Read Pointer points to the next flit that is retransmitted.

The receiver contains the RRSM, and it provides the mechanism for the following state variable to keep track of the sequence number of the next flit to arrive.

■ ESeq - This indicates the expected sequence number of the next valid flit at the receiving link layer entity. ESeq is incremented by one (modulo the size of retry buffer) on error-free reception of an idle flit or an info flit. ESeq stops incrementing after an error is detected on a received flit until an LLR.Ack message is received. ESeq is initialized to 0 at link reset.

Note | *In contrast to some of the other protocols, the sequence number is not prepended to a flit or packet. The sequence number is "managed" from reset. During the retry sequence, the receiver provides the sequence number to start the re-transmission.*

Normal Operation of the Link Layer Retry Mechanism

In standard operation of the link, the link layer retry buffer stores every protocol layer flit and every link layer credit return packet, which can be termed "retriable" flits. The write pointer points to the next available entry in the retry buffer to store these outbound flits. Excluding credit bearing flits, no link layer special flits are stored in the retry buffer. The most common of the link layer special flits would be the Null flit; these do not enter the retry buffer because they carry no information.

In the case where the Write pointer equals the Tail pointer, the retry buffer is completely full and no retriable flit can be sent until the reception of an Ack from the remote receiver. During this time, only Null flits and other non-retriable link layer flits can be sent by the transmitter. The reception of an Ack signals that eight retriable flits have been received without error at the other end of the link. This allows the Tail pointer to advance forward by eight, permitting up to eight more retriable flits to be sent.

Acks can be carried in all protocol layer packet header flits, as well as the link layer credit bearing Idle flit. Note in the Idle flit, multiple Acks can be returned at a time.

Link Layer Retry Recovery Operation Flow

In the case where the receiver detects a CRC error, the LRSM executes the following actions:

- Starts dropping all incoming retriable flits.
- Signals to the transmitter of the local link layer to issue a Link Layer Retry Request (LLR.Req), including the sequence number (the start of retriable sequence), which encodes the location of the error flit in the remote retry buffer.
- After the LLR.Req is sent, the LRSM begins looking for a Link Layer Retry Acknowledgement flit (LLR.Ack).
- Upon the reception of LLR.Ack, flits subsequent to it represent the start of the retried sequence, so normal receiver operations resume.

When an LLR.Req is received the RRSM executes the following actions:

- ■ Signals the transmitter to stop sending new flits.
- ■ Sets the Read Pointer of the Retry Buffer to the sequence number encoded in the LLR.Req.
- ■ Injects an LLR.Ack into the transmitter, followed by the flits from the Retry Buffer starting at the Read Pointer.
  - – The retried flits are those stored between the Read and Write Pointer of the Retry Buffer.
  - – After all retried flits have been sent, the transmitter is allowed to resume sending of new flits.

For debug and diagnostic purposes, the status of the link level retry mechanism is provided in an Intel QPI–architected link layer status register. This register provides software with access to information such as the utilization of the retry buffer, how many retries have been attempted, and whether the LRSM is currently processing an error.

The flow above represents a "typical" Intel QPI link level retry, but it by no means describes all the possible actions that may occur as more difficult error scenarios are encountered.

Physical Layer Re-initialization

In some situations, the back up and retry process may fail to recover from the event. Incoming flits may still result in incorrect CRC checks. In that case, the link layer contains counters that can be configured to control how many times to attempt the retry process. Once that counter expires, a more drastic measure can be taken. The link layer can force the physical layer to go back through its initialization process. This will once again determine the working lanes, establish optimal bit and phit synchronization, and bring the physical connection back up to the L0 state. From this fresh start, the retry process resumes. Counters can be used to control how many times this is attempted.

It is worth noting that other than a slight time delay, this physical layer re-initialization process is transparent to the layers above the link layer. All pending messages are held and once the link is operating properly the normal flow of information resumes. No information is lost during the process. Other than logging the event in system status logs, no software action is required.

Interleaving

Within a message class, packet transmission takes place consecutively with respect to other packets. That is, if a packet occupies 11 flits, all 11 would be transmitted one after the other down the connection. In some situations, these longer packets may need to be interrupted in order to allow shorter high priority messages to go through. To facilitate this interleaving of packets, Intel QPI packets have a bit (termed IIB) that identifies the beginning of a packet that may be interleaved into another. The two allowed forms of interleaving are as shown in Figure 3.17.

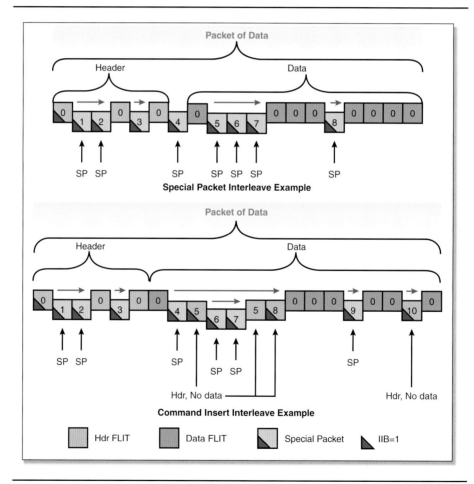

Figure 3.17 Two Forms of Packet Interleaving

Special packet interleaving is supported by all Intel QPI devices. This technique allows for any of the SPC messages to be inserted into the middle of a longer packet, a data packet in this example. In flit 0, the data packet starts as indicated by the setting of its IIB bit. Immediately following are two SPC messages, each of which has the IIB set. The remaining portion of the Data packet (consisting of some header and then data flits) continues, with several additional SPC messages shown interleaved along the way.

Command insert interleaving is an optional capability that allows the insertion of certain protocol level messages, such as SNP or NDR packets, into the middle of any packet with a data payload. The bottom portion of Figure 3.17 illustrates one example of this and in fact shows a double nesting where SPC packets could be embedded within the command packet being inserted. Packets 1, 2, 3, 4, 5, 8, 9 and 10 are nested packets. Packets 6 and 7 are double nested packets.

Packet Formats

In the Intel QuickPath architecture, the link layer is where the packets are defined and their contents are specified. This section identifies all the different packet types and gives a functional definition of their contents.

Strict Encapsulation Is Not Used

Some communications interfaces (like Ethernet) encapsulate the ultimate payload in a series of wrappers. Each layer adds its own header and trailers to the information passed down to it from the higher layers. In a similar manner, the receiving agent would unwrap each of the headers and trailers, using the information utilitzed by that layer, and then pass the results on up the stack. Ultimately the original payload or message is delivered to the end agent.

Intel QPI packet formats do not fully follow this wrapper approach and the layers are in a sense more tightly integrated than a pure layered approach would allow. The advantage is an efficient packet structure that can be used to quickly communicate information between the agents. The possible disadvantage is that this is a less modular approach. Since Intel QPI devices typically implement the layers of the architecture within the hardware elements of a given device, the factors of implementation efficiency and performance were deemed more important than adhering to a strictly modular design approach.

Intel QPI Packets—One or More Flits

Figure 3.18 again shows the basic format of a flit or flow control unit. Recall that flits are the fundamental unit of transfer between link layers. The flit shown in Figure 3.18 is in full-width format with four phits of 20 lanes each. The content of the flit in a generic sense consists of a 72 bit payload and the 8 bit CRC.

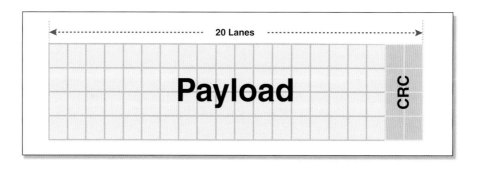

Figure 3.18 A Flit – Building Block for Packets

The flit is also the fundamental building block of packets, which are the messages exchanged by the higher layers. Packets are formed from at least one flit, and can contain multiple flits. Packets always contain an integral number of flits (for example: 1, 2, 3, … 9, and so on). Partial flits are not allowed.

Defined Packets and Their Contents

The different types of packets defined in the Intel QuickPath Architecture are shown in Table 3.2. Also shown are the type groupings. Different devices have the flexibility to choose to support specific groupings of packets, called Packet Types 1, 2, and 3. The choice of which packet type to use in a specific component design is based primarily on the set of features and expandability goals of a particular platform. While Table 3.2 contains identical entries for Type 1 and Type 2 packets, the actual contents of these packets differs slightly between the two types. In particular, Type 2 packets contain more bits for the NodeID fields. These additional bits give systems using Type 2 packets more expandability in terms of the number of agents they can support. Note that all devices communicating over Intel QPI in a given platform would be configured in some manner to be using the same Packet Type grouping. SPC packets are not shown in this table due to their limited use for link layer management.

Table 3.2 Packet Names and Type Groupings

Packet Name	Definition	Type 1 Packet?	Type 2 Packet?	Type 3 Packet?
SA	Standard Address	Yes	Yes	
SCA	Standard Coherence Address	Yes	Yes	
SCC	Standard Coherence, No Address	Yes	Yes	
SCD	Standard Complete with Data	Yes	Yes	
EA	Extended Address	Yes	Yes	Yes
ECA	Extended Coherence Address			Yes
ECC	Extended Coherence, No Address			Yes
ECD	Extended Complete with Data			Yes
EIC	Extended I/O Command	Yes	Yes	Yes
NCM	Non-Coherent Message	Yes	Yes	Yes
SDR	Standard Data Response	Yes	Yes	
SDW	Standard Data Write	Yes	Yes	
EDR	Extended Data Response			Yes
EDW	Extended Data Write			Yes
EBDW	Extended Byte Enable Data Write	Yes	Yes	Yes
PtPT	Peer to Peer Tunnel	Yes	Yes	Yes

Headers and Data Flits

Command packets are formed by choosing one of the available packet names (also may be referred to as the header) from the list above. These packets do not contain a data payload.

Data flits consist of 64 bits of data, 8 bits of CRC and of the remaining 8 bits some are used for control and error checking. A data packet is formed by combining one of the appropriate packet name headers (such as SDR or EDR) and adding 8 data flits.

Basic Contents of a Packet

All packets carry certain information fields. These fields include the message class, the transaction opcode, Destination Node ID (DNID), the virtual network, credit information, a transaction identifier, and the Ack field used in LLR.

In addition to this common content, each specific packet type contains information relevant to that type of message. Table 3.3 identifies this content for the Type 2 grouping of packet types.

Table 3.3 Type 2 Packets and Content

Field	Packet Type										
	SA	SCA	SCC	SCD	EA	NCM	EIC	SDR	SDW	EBDW	PtPT
Number of Flits	1	1	1	1	2	3	3	1	1	3	3
Address	45:6	40:6	11:6	11:6	45:0	none	45:3	11:6	45:6	45:3	none
Poison						Yes	Yes			Yes	Yes
RSNID		Yes	Yes								
FCTID			Yes								
Rsp Data State								Yes			
Rsp_Status			Yes	Yes				Yes			
PCLS								Yes			
ReqState								Yes			
CRT					Yes		Yes				
Length					Yes						
Message Type						Yes					
Parameters/ Data				24b		72b	64b				128b
Byte Enables						8b	8b			64b	
Tunnel Type											Yes
Reserved or Fixed			21b	8b	56b	94b	62b	23b		73b	48b

Specific Fields

In this section we describe a few of the fields mentioned above, and that are carried in certain packets.

Node IDs

Every unique agent on the Intel QPI is assigned a Node ID. This multi-bit field is used to identify which agents are involved in the transfer. RSNID for example is the Requester or Sender Node ID. DNID is the Destination Node ID that eventually will consume the packet.

Address

This is the Address of the global memory space addressed by all Intel QPI agents. Coherent transactions are cache-line size aligned to 64B boundaries. Certain packets may carry all or portions of the Address field.

Message Class

This field identifies which of the six possible message classes applies to this transaction.

Response Data State

This field identifies in what coherency state (M, E, S, I, or F) the data is being returned. The receiving caching agent uses this information to help set the state of its internal caching structure for that line of data.

Opcode

The Protocol layer uses the opcode field in conjunction with the message class field to form a complete opcode. The link layer uses this opcode to distinguish between home agent target or caching agent target for messages when a home agent and a caching agent share the same NodeID. Additionally the link layer uses the opcode to determine the packet size.

Table 3.4 lists several pieces of information relevant to forming a packet. The columns define the message class and the rows are the opcodes. Within each cell of the table there may be a transaction name given. These are the protocol layer transactions that the link layer is being asked to form and then communicate with the other agent. Each transaction type is also mapped to a particular packet format (EA, SA, SDR, and so on) as shown in the cells.

Table 3.4   Protocol Layer Transaction Names, Message Classes, and Opcodes

Opcode	SNP Class	HOM Class - Requests	HOM Class - Responses	DRS Class	NDR Class	NCB Class
Primary Format	SA/EA	SA/EA	SCA/ECA or SCC/ECC (C)	SDR/EDR or SDW/EDW (W) or EBDW	SCC/ECC or SCD/ECD (D)	Several
0000	SnpCur	RdCur	RspI	DataC_(X)	Gnt_Cmp	NcWr (W)
0001	SnpCode	RdCode	RspS	DataC_(X)_FrcAckCnflt	Gnt_FrcAckCnflt	WcWr (W)
0010	SnpData	RdData		DataC_(X)_Cmp		
0011		NonSnpRd		DataNc		
0100	SnpInvOwn	RdInvOwn	RspCnflt (C)	WbIData (W)	CmpD (D)	
0101	SnpInvXtoI	InvXtoI		WbSData (W)	AbortTO (D)	
0110		EvctCln	RspCnfltOwn (C)	WbEData (W)		
0111		NonSnpWr		NonSnpWrData (W)		
1000	SnpInvItoE	InvItoE	RspFwd	WbIDataPtl (EBDW)	Cmp	NcMsgB (NCM)
1001		AckCnfltWbI	RspFwdI		FrcAckCnflt	IntLogical (EBDW)
1010			RspFwdS	WbEDataPtl (EBDW)	Cmp_FwdCode	IntPhysical (EBDW)
1011			RspFwdIWb	NonSnpWrDataPtl (EBDW)	Cmp_FwdInvOwn	IntPrioUpd (EBDW)
1100		WbMtoI	RspFwdSWb		Cmp_FwdInvItoE	NcWrPtl (EBDW)
1101		WbMtoE	RspIWb			WcWrPtl (EBDW)
1110		WbMtoS	RspSWb			NcP2PB (PtPT)
1111		AckCnflt				

Note: All undefined opcodes are reserved for future use.

Putting It All Together

To form the packets then, the link layer starts with the requested transaction type coming from the Protocol layer. From Table 3.4 we can see that each transaction type maps to a particular packet name and also to a fixed opcode. For example, an RdCode request would use the SA (or EA for Type 3 systems) packet format with an opcode of 0001. The link layer then fills in all the other information fields specified by the SA/EA packet format. This would include the address, Node IDs, any credit or Ack information, and other content as shown in Table 3.3. The end result is a 1 (or 2 for EA) flit packet that can be delivered across the interconnect.

Controlling the Features

The preceding sections have described many of the features and capabilities of the physical and link layers of the Intel QuickPath Interconnect. This section discusses the ways in which several of those capabilities can be selected and controlled. This allows the interconnect to be adapted to the particular platform requirements that exist in actual use.

Physical Layer Configuration

The physical layer performs many functions automatically as part of its initialization process. This is essential because a platform may not be able to operate at all, at least not in terms of executing any software, until at least one link is established.

Initial Operating Speed

As mentioned previously, by default current implementations of Intel QPI links begin operation at a slow speed that is specified as one fourth the rate of the device's reference clock input. At this operational speed, no additional configuration is needed in order to proceed through the physical and link layer initialization. All necessary L0 operational functions are provided at this lower speed. All link layer functions are also functional except for the link low power states. This initial operating speed is expected to be used to allow the platform firmware to execute and configure system resources for full operation. Setting a full speed operational mode is part of that configuration.

Working Lanes and Link Width

Early in the physical layer state machine, working data and clock lanes are automatically identified. Any nonfunctional or even nonexistent lanes are detected by the hardware and mapped out accordingly. Devices that are designed to support less than full-width link operation can then continue in either half- or quarter-width link modes.

The selection of the link width is determined by the exchange of a Width Capability Indicator (WCI) parameter. This is done by the hardware on both sides of the link and they use this parameter to choose the optimal link width based on each device's capabilities and the working lanes. No platform firmware intervention is required and no hardware strapping options are needed, the link hardware can configure itself based on the conditions it detects on the link.

Retraining Intervals and Durations

The process of reestablishing bit level synchronization takes place periodically during the L0 and L0s operational states. Two factors must be agreed upon by both sides of the link in order for this routine retraining to occur correctly. The two factors are the retraining interval and the retraining duration. The interval controls how much time elapses between retraining events, the duration determines how long the retraining pattern is applied. Both of these factors are exchanged by the physical layer hardware as part of the Config state interaction. Once completed the two sides will be in agreement regarding the values they will use for those two factors. Platform firmware can adjust those parameters through the setting of certain control registers and a subsequent re-initialization of the physical layer. Initial default settings however are sufficient for correct operation so the changing of these parameters is primarily for fine tuning of the retraining schedule.

Lane Reversal and Polarity Inversion

Both of these capabilities are automatically configured by the physical layer. If the PCB wiring introduces either of these, it will be detected during link initialization and adjustments will be made in the hardware. No board level hardware configuration (such as strapping options) is needed and no firmware configuration is required.

Full Speed Operation

Other than the slow mode of operation, the physical layer is agnostic regarding the exact speed of the transfers on the link. The speed at which the link operates is generally determined in current products by register settings in the devices which control PLL and clock ratios driving the internal logic. The electrical sub-block of the physical layer is aware of these speed settings as they influence the transmission and reception of the phits. Both sides of the link would have settings which yield the same speed of link operation, 6.4 GT/s for example. Setting of these registers is done in a device or platform specific manner. One common method would be through system firmware programming those registers while the link is operating in slow mode. The new speed settings take effect once the physical layer goes through a software initiated reset and the connection is reestablished.

Physical Layer Device Registers

While details are device-specific, several control and status registers (CSRs) can be used to influence the operation of the physical layer. In general these registers provide information about the device capabilities, allow the control of certain functions, and provide status about those functions. These functions may be of interest to the platform's operation, or useful in debug and validation situations. Examples of these register settings include:

- The ability to determine if a device can support reduced width operation.

- The ability to turn off certain features to enable platform debug or testing.

- The ability to single step through device link initialization, or to reset the physical layer and perform the process again.

- The ability to determine which lanes were detected during the init process and to disable certain parts of the link if desired.

- Status bits that show the current state of the init process, as well as the state of the previous initialization.

- Registers for the implementation of certain self-test capabilities such as pattern generation and loop-back.

Control and Status Register (CSR) Access

While the details are outside the scope of this chapter, the CSRs can be accessed through in-band transactions over the Intel QPI. The interconnect supports specific transaction types that can perform read and write operations of the CSRs within a device. In this manner the startup firmware running on the bootstrap processor of a platform can configure device registers in itself and in other devices such that regular platform operation can begin. Alternatively, some components support a sideband method of accessing these registers. This would typically be through a JTAG or SMBUS compliant serial interface, driven through external logic or a service processor.

Link Layer Configuration

During its initialization process, the two communicating link layers do exchange information related to device configuration. Some of these parameters affect the device operation automatically while others are captured in status registers for later use. So in contrast to the physical layer configuration, which tended to be almost totally automatic and hardware centric, Link layer configuration involves an interaction between the hardware and the platform firmware. The usage of some of this captured information is described in more depth in the next chapter. Here we discuss the type of information captured and how it is used at the hardware level.

LLR Control

Certain parameters have an effect on the link Level retry process at the hardware level. For example, the size of the retry buffer at a device's transmitter is design-specific and may vary from one device to the next. As part of the parameter exchange, each device indicates the size of its LLR buffer so that the hardware can take that into account during link operation.

Low Power Modes

Parameters are exchanged to indicate the ability of a device to support the L0s and L1 low power modes.

CRC Mode to Use

An optional extended mode of CRC generation and calculation is supported by some devices. This is known as the Rolling-CRC mode because the calculation is performed continuously over two consecutive flits. Parameters are exchanged that identify each device's abilities in this area. Based on those parameters the link chooses either the normal or the Rolling-CRC mode.

Optional Interleave Support

This parameter indicates a device is capable of performing the Command Insert Interleave, which is an optional capability.

Agent Type Identifiers

Each agent provides an 8-bit field that identifies the basic functionality of the agent connected to the link. The parameter is also encoded with NodeID information so if a device on the link contains multiple NodeIDs, the functions can all be identified. Example agent types include: home agent, caching agent, I/O agent, firmware agent, and configuration agent. Note that a device such as a processor may contain multiple agents.

Parameter Capture

The parameters exchanged during link layer initialization are captured in a set of status registers. Other than the direct hardware configuration effects that this information can have, these registers serve to provide this information to platform firmware responsible for configuration of the entire platform during the boot process. The next chapter elaborates on how those parameters are used.

Link Layer Device Registers

Again, while details are device-specific, several control and status registers can be used to influence the operation of the link layer. In general these registers provide information about the device capabilities, allow the control of certain functions, and provide status about those functions. These functions may be of interest to the platform's operation, or useful in debug and validation situations. Examples of these register settings include:

- Status bits that indicate the size of the available credit pools for the VN0, VN1, and VNA virtual networks.

- Status bits regarding which CRC and interleave mode is supported.

- Control bits that enable the usage of the low power modes L0s and L1.

- Control bits used for debug of link layer initialization events.

- Control bits that determine the value of various counters used in the LLR process. This includes the maximum number of retry attempts, timeout values, and maximum number of physical layer re-initialization attempts.

- Status bits that show the current state of the LLR queue, and the state from the last initialization.

- Status bits that capture how many events take place during the LLR process.

- Status bits indicating how many credits are currently available.

- Parameter exchange information is captured in a set of registers.

Summary

This chapter has described the process by which two devices can get connected together on the Intel QuickPath Interconnect in order that they may then use that connection for higher level message traffic. The physical and link layer functions have been described, along with the process they follow to get initialized. In the next chapter we explore how this connection is used to support the process of getting a computer system through the boot process.

Chapter 4

System Initialization

Reacting to the news that Maine and Texas had been connected by telegraph lines—the point at issue is not whether Maine and Texas may now talk to one another, but rather whether they have anything significant to say.

— Henry David Thoreau

In the previous chapter, we described the process by which two components based on Intel® QuickPath Interconnect (Intel QPI) technology establish a connection between themselves. At that point they can reliably send information back and forth. But as the quote above asks, what shall we do with that connection? This chapter describes the first steps in the effective use of those communication pathways, the process of initializing the entire system so that the machine can perform the overall function for which it was intended.

Basic Concepts

The beginning of the platform initialization process is to apply power, stabilize all critical clocking circuits, and then control the release of various *reset* signals so that the computing system will begin operation in a predictable and controlled manner. In this context, *Reset* is defined to be a set of hardware-based events that establishes an initial hardware state. *Initialization* is defined to be the set of instruction sequences that follow Reset and which prepare the hardware for execution of boot firmware. The *boot firmware* then prepares the system for the loading of and transferring control to an operating system. A significant goal of these hardware and boot firmware activities is to get their tasks completed and get out of the way so that control can be handed over to an operating system as soon as possible.

Platforms based on the Intel QuickPath Architecture are no different in that basic regard, but they do have several additional capabilities that are vital to the task of getting started. These interconnect features are essential in supporting the wide variety of platform configurations that are served by these systems. These features also introduce new areas that the boot firmware in particular needs to be concerned about, things that either did not exist in previous platforms or that were not as configurable in how they operated. These areas include:

- *Link resource initialization* – Some links may require configuration and explicit startup instructions; others may come up automatically. In either case, some links may fail to initialize at all, or could come up in a reduced operational state.

- *Topology discovery* – Certain devices may or may not be populated, or may not be fully functional. A policy for discovering all the interconnected resources must be devised and implemented.

- *Distributed memory configuration* – There typically would be multiple memory controllers, each of which could be controlling a differing amount of physical memory.

In all of the above areas, an Intel QPI system opens up new possibilities in how these issues can or should be handled. The following sections outline the basic steps for many of these initialization actions. Later sections in this chapter provide more details on how these actions can take place. The approach taken in this chapter is to define and describe these building blocks of the initialization process, but we do not prescribe a specific formula for how the overall boot process is performed. There are several ways to put these blocks together and still accomplish the overall task of getting ready to run the operating system. Those choices are left to the platform architects and development teams.

Before Software Runs

Of course, the goal of initializing the computing system is to enable useful work to be conducted, to allow the processors to execute the operating system and application programs that they are intended to execute. In order for that to take place, many things must be operational prior to the initial code fetch from the reset vector. As we shall see, there are many possibilities to choose from and several things that the hardware design takes care of prior to handing over control to the boot firmware.

Multiple Reset Domains

Systems based on Intel QPI are expected to continue to operate in the presence of certain conditions that could result in system downtime if not for the error recovery features. They also are called upon to support sophisticated operating system features such as dynamic reconfiguration and partitioning. In order to facilitate those advanced features, the hardware is designed to be able to independently control the resetting and initialization of portions of the hardware without disrupting other portions. As we shall see in later sections, the control of these resets may take place by portions of the Intel QPI layers, for example the link layer may force a reset of the physical layer. Or these reset functions may take place under control of boot firmware or other layers of software, using control registers to influence the hardware.

Boot Modes

Platform designers may have multiple choices in terms of how the boot firmware device is connected to the system. A common choice for smaller-scale systems is to use a firmware hub (FWH), which is connected to the ICH device and then to the legacy IOH device (LIOH). The LIOH in turn is connected through at least one Intel QPI link to the processor(s).

Figure 4.1 depicts a two processor and single IOH configuration with the FWH logically connected through the ICH to the only IOH, which by default is the legacy IOH. We have seen this basic diagram before; what is added here are the ICH and FWH connections. The hardware typically would initialize itself such that transactions from either CPU can reach the FWH.

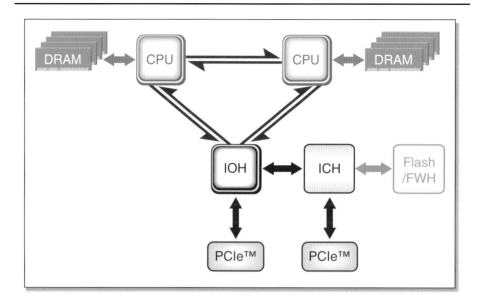

Figure 4.1   Dual CPU, Single IOH System Topology

Figure 4.2 shows a more complex four processor dual IOH configuration. In this configuration, two of the CPUs are not directly connected to the LIOH but instead are one Intel QPI "hop" distant from the LIOH.

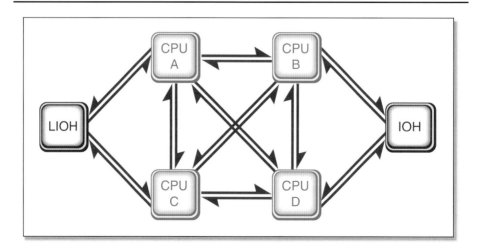

Figure 4.2   Four Processor, Dual IOH Topology

In both of these platform examples, the processor hardware configures itself so that initial code fetches will be successful. The hardware initializes itself since the boot firmware is not executing yet. Booting in this manner is termed the Intel QPI *link boot mode* since the firmware is located across an Intel QPI link relative to the processor.

Other platform-specific boot modes may include a firmware storage device connected directly to the processor socket. Another option is to rely on an external system service processor that has the ability to independently initialize internal Control and Status Registers (CSRs) of all devices and to control the reset and bring-up of the platform. In the rest of this chapter, we focus only on the Intel QPI link boot mode because this is the most common method for small and medium-scale systems as shown in Figures 4.1 and 4.2.

Bringing Up the Link

Before any software can execute, a connection pathway to the memory device that contains the boot firmware code must be established. Since platform configurations may vary, the hardware itself establishes this pathway so that the boot firmware can then proceed. Note that in some cases the "hardware" could also encompass microcode or other unique initialization functions that may exist as part of the overall processor device. The processor hardware and any low level microcode work together to create the connection used during the rest of the boot firmware startup process.

One step in this process is to initialize the Intel QPI link(s) that are in the path between the processor and the boot firmware storage device. Various platforms may make different provisions in this regard. Simple configurations may allow only a specific pathway while more complex platform topologies may allow multiple options for making this connection. In any event, the link(s) are brought up to the L0 operational state as discussed in Chapter 3. Once this has been done, the processor core can issue instruction fetches which flow across the interconnect to the hardware controlling the firmware storage device.

In addition to the link initialization, various control and status registers are set to default values so that basic functionality of the device is accomplished. Part of this is noting any functions that are not operational. For example, any

Intel QPI links that fail to train to the L0 state are noted. This is the case if a processor socket is not populated. Any other processors note that the links going to that unpopulated socket are not operational.

Setting the Route

Recall that transactions on the Intel QPI fabric are routed according to a destination Node ID. Every function therefore is assigned a unique Node ID and the routing tables that define the rules for routing the transactions are initialized. Smaller-scale platforms may make some simplifying assumptions in order to facilitate this process. Larger-scale configurations generally allow more flexibility. In either case, in this link boot mode, the processor device typically must establish these Node IDs and routing tables without the use of boot firmware, at least until an initial pathway has been created and the boot firmware can begin execution.

Selecting Processors for Specific Tasks

Each processor socket in these platforms typically contains multiple CPU cores that can each execute their own instruction stream independently. At system initialization, however, some steps must be performed in a very controlled manner. This requires that certain functions be limited to only execute on a subset of the total number of processor cores. That subset could be as small as one in some cases. Generally speaking, any of the available cores can be selected to perform these functions. Details of how these selections are made are covered later in this chapter.

Processor Bootstrap Processor (PBSP)

This is the logical processor (a single core) responsible for initialization and operation of the socket in which the PBSP resides.

System Bootstrap Processor (SBSP)

This is the logical processor (a single core) responsible for the bulk of system-level initialization. This encompasses multiple processor sockets, multiple IOH devices, and other system resources such as memory, which typically are initialized prior to handoff to the operating system.

Application Processor (AP)

Application processors (APs) are those processor cores which do not participate in the system initialization process unless they are directed to do so by the SBSP.

What Is Out There? Topology Discovery

When the system first comes out of reset and the boot firmware starts executing, one of the primary tasks is to discover what resources are available and how they are interconnected. The various hardware functions play a role in this, as do the PBSPs while they configure the processor sockets individually. It is the SBSP however that then examines the information it has available, and goes through a methodical process to determine what resources exist, which ones are functional, and then configures those resources in preparation for the operating system. This process is referred to as *topology discovery.*

Intel® QuickPath Interconnect Layer Setup

After determining the system topology and the range of available resources, the SBSP has the task of configuring specific functions of each of the Intel QPI layers. Some default settings are established by the hardware and these are sufficient for at least a subset of the links to be used for initial boot firmware functions. Beyond that it is up to the boot firmware itself, running on the PBSP, to configure the various control registers and to judiciously control the reset of various layers in order for new configuration settings to take effect.

Link Speed Transition

As mentioned in Chapter 3, the physical characteristics of the interconnect generally require specific equalization settings to be established on a per-link basis before full speed operation can commence. Therefore, the Intel QPI links by default will come up in an initial slow mode, which is a 66.66-mega-transfers/second (MT/s) rate. At the slow mode transfer rate the links will still train and operate in the L0 state, but there is no need for any platform-specific tuning. Part of the boot process then is to determine the desired full operational speed of the links, configure the necessary resources that control that speed, and then perform a controlled physical layer reset to bring the new speed into effect.

Rest of Boot Firmware

Once the system initialization process has completed all of the steps outlined above, all of the Intel QPI–specific items will have been configured and are operational. The communication fabric can then be used by the boot firmware in order to perform the remaining initialization functions that are not directly involved with the Intel QPI fabric. A big part of the remaining work is the task of memory system initialization and configuration. The final step is to synchronize all processors and turn over control to the operating system, optionally through the extensible firmware interface (EFI) layer. Such tasks are well understood in the context of multiple processor systems and they are not specific to Intel QPI. As such they will not be discussed in the rest of this chapter.

Actions Prior to Boot Firmware Execution

The primary action to be taken at this point is to establish the path to the device that contains the boot firmware. As shown in Figure 4.1 and 4.2, a boot firmware storage device (FWH) is typically connected to the ICH device that in turn is connected to the legacy IOH (LIOH). Other system configurations are possible, especially for large-scale servers, but for this discussion we shall consider only the Intel QPI link boot case. The issue then is how to configure the processor's system interface logic along with the LIOH logic so that the core's code fetch operation succeeds and the boot firmware can continue with platform setup.

Multiple Reset Domains

The first step is to come out of reset so that the hardware can begin executing. Because certain features require the ability to independently control reset to different hardware portions of the machine, Intel QPI devices are designed to accommodate multiple forms of reset.

Cold or Power-Good Reset

This type of reset affects all hardware elements of the platform. As the name implies, Power-Good reset occurs with the de-assertion of a hardware signal to the device when the power is stable. All hardware elements revert to their default state and no information is preserved from any previous power on state.

Device Level Reset

In this form of reset, the power supplies to all devices have remained steady, so the state can be preserved to some extent across this reset event. As we shall see later in this chapter, this type of reset allows system firmware to perform some amount of component initialization that is then "sticky" across the device reset.

Device reset can be caused by hardware signals if the platform is designed to manipulate the reset signals externally. The most common form of a device reset would be triggered by the boot firmware writing to a control register in the LIOH (or possibly elsewhere). This action then causes an external signal to toggle and resets the device.

Physical Layer Reset

As a general rule, Intel QPI devices have the ability to independently reset various layers of the interface. In particular the link and physical layers are able to be reset without affecting the state of the rest of the machine. A physical layer reset is used when the intent is to force that layer to reestablish proper low-level synchronization between the two components, possibly involving a change in some of the operating characteristics of that interface. Some typical uses of this form of reset include: a change in operational speed, recovery from severe bit error events, or recovery from loss of part of the physical connection. Reset of the physical layer has no impact on the actual information being conveyed across the link since all error checking, flow control, and data interpretation is done at the higher layers.

Physical layer reset can be caused by any of several possible actions. Writing to a physical layer control register is one common method used by the boot firmware. Losing the incoming forwarded clock is interpreted as an Inband reset and causes a physical layer reset. Internal mechanisms also exist that allow the link layer logic to force a physical layer reset, typically triggered if excessive CRC errors have been detected.

Link Layer Reset

Link layer reset is generally used whenever certain parameters of the link layer must be changed. After a Power-Good reset, the link layer capabilities are in their default state. In order to use certain functions such as low-power modes, non-default credit allocations, or Rolling CRC mode, the link layer is reconfigured and then reset. The new settings take effect after the reset.

Link layer reset is done by writing to a control register. Note that more care must be taken when resetting the link layer than with a physical layer reset. This is because the link layer does maintain information that is critical to the correct information exchange between agents. Improper use of this reset would cause incorrect system operation, so link layer reset is used judiciously.

Partition Level Reset

The final level of reset is a reset applied to an entire operating system partition. Intel QPI platforms can support running multiple instances of an operating system on different portions of the hardware. For example in Figure 4.2, two of the CPUs could be running one partition while the other two run a second partition. It is also possible that different operating systems coexist, each using its own resources. In such an environment the platform can provide mechanisms for resetting one of the partitions without affecting the remaining resources. From the Intel QPI fabric perspective, this ability relies upon the multiple reset domains described above. From the operating system perspective, there is obviously much more involved and that is outside the scope of this book. Chapter 6 contains more information on the topic of partitions in the section on dynamic reconfiguration.

Boot Modes

Processors based on Intel QPI technology are designed to handle various boot modes as dictated by the needs of the platform environment they are required to operate in. For example a small dual-processor socket system may only support the Intel QPI link boot mode as mentioned previously. Larger servers typically contain some sort of independent system service processor, or may have requirements that dictate the use of directly connected firmware. The component design teams take these requirements into account when creating the hardware for the processor and other devices.

Generally speaking the boot mode for a processor is either fixed by the hardware design, or has a platform-specific method of selecting which boot mode will be used. Intel processors designed for the configuration shown in Figure 4.1 for example may be designed to always (and only) use the Intel QPI link boot mode. Each processor "knows" to look for the boot firmware code by sending transactions down the Intel QPI link connected to the LIOH. We will describe how that is determined later in this chapter.

In a similar manner, processors designed to go into the configuration shown in Figure 4.2 typically would allow multiple boot modes. The boot mode actually used may be determined through the use of hardware strapping options on the processors. As the processor comes out of reset, the state of that strap is sensed and then the boot flow proceeds accordingly. In the Intel QPI link boot mode, each processor proceeds as in the two socket case, by sending transactions over the Intel QPI fabric to the LIOH. In this configuration however, there may be intermediate hops through an adjacent processor socket in order to access the LIOH. This limits the ability of the processors that are not connected directly to the LIOH. Specifically, those processors (CPU B and CPU D in Figure 4.2) cannot become the SBSP. In fact they typically wait for the SBSP to configure the various Intel QPI resources before they can begin execution; they will stay in a wait loop until the resource configuration has been completed.

Physical Layer Actions

In the Intel QPI link boot mode, the processor hardware typically triggers the initialization of the physical and link layers without waiting for any sort of boot firmware action. Links will train up to the L0 operational state if they are functioning correctly. Link layer initialization including the parameter exchange functions will also take place. In addition, certain address decoding functions are initialized so that the initial code fetches can be directed to the proper destination. As mentioned in Chapter 3, the physical layer starts off in the slow mode transfer rate. The link can remain in this mode for as long as necessary although the expectation is that a transition to full-speed operation will be performed as soon as possible.

Link Layer Initialization

Link layer initialization takes place after the physical layer on the component has reached the L0 state. The link layer state machine proceeds through a set of handshake actions that eventually result in the link being ready for normal operation. A key function during this process is the exchange of certain parameters between the two agents. Each agent generates a set of parameters, sometimes called link exchange parameters (LEPs) and the receiving agent captures that information into certain control and status registers. In some cases these parameters directly control the operation of the link layer hardware. Standard or Rolling CRC mode selection is an example of this. In other cases the parameters provide useful information to the boot firmware so that the firmware can make the correct decisions when configuring the hardware resources for the platform.

The LEP values contain several items useful for system configuration as well as others that inform the system as to the link layer's capabilities. One of the primary uses of the LEP information is the *topology discovery* process, which is described later in this chapter. The captured LEP values include:

- The sender's port number
- Multiple agent type indicators: home, caching, I/O proxy, or firmware agent are common types
- Portions of the sender's Node ID
- Status bits indicating support levels for low-power modes L0 and L1
- Status bits indicating which CRC modes are supported and preferred by the sender
- The size of the sender's Link Level Retry buffer

In addition to the captured LEP values, status registers exist for both the physical and link layers. The contents of these registers indicate the end result of the initialization process. Normal operation is the expected status, abnormal results are also captured in the status registers and can be used to record problems.

Node IDs

Determining the proper Node ID information to be used for Intel QPI transactions is an essential part of the configuration process. The correct settings for these values are determined by a combination of component design, hardware actions based on platform configuration, configuration strapping on the device, and possibly the firmware or service processor setting configuration register bits. Each component has particular methods that are suited to the needs of the platform that component was designed to service.

Small-Scale Platform Node ID Convention

While a small platform is not required to follow the convention described here, this method is how current Intel processors and IOH devices used in the configuration shown in Figure 4.1 perform their Node ID assignment.

The process relies on the LEP values as described above, in particular the sender's port number. Currently, each processor and IOH in this type of platform requires one Node ID. By default the LIOH Node ID is set to 0. During the LEP exchange, each processor captures the LEP values from the IOH and from the other processor. This allows the processor to determine which one of its links is connected to the IOH, and which one goes to the second processor. A Socket ID (and APIC ID) for each processor is then assigned based on the port number of the IOH that connects to that processor. Detecting an LEP value indicating port 0 implies that the Socket ID for that processor will become 0. Likewise, the processor connected to IOH port 1 will become Socket ID 1. The Node ID for each processor is then computed as:

Socket_ID + Node_ID_IOH +1.

Referring back again to Figure 4.1, assume that the IOH port on the left side is Port 0 and that the IOH Node ID is also 0. The Node ID assignment algorithm will result in the left CPU getting Node ID = 1 (0+0+1) and the right CPU getting Node ID = 2 (1+0+1). In this case, hardware takes care of setting this information; no boot firmware or user intervention is required. Note that this algorithm works regardless of which physical port on the processors or the IOH is actually used. The board layout is not constrained in terms of connecting specific ports together in this platform.

Medium-Scale Platform Node ID Convention

Again, while a medium-scale platform is not required to follow the convention described here, this method of assigning Node IDs is used by certain current Intel processors and IOH devices that have been designed for the configuration shown in Figure 4.2.

In this case, additional functions within the processor require more Node IDs per socket to be assigned. The lower order two bits of the Node IDs are determined by the hardware design and cannot be changed. Higher order bits are set by strapping options on the printed circuit board. When coming out of reset the processor captures these values into internal hardware. The processor then advertises the entire Node ID value as part of the LEP process. No computation algorithm is required but this method does require strapping pins on the processor to be set correctly. In this platform, the LIOH is given a Node ID of 0 and the second IOH would get a Node ID of 4. A total of eleven Node IDs are used to identify all functions in this platform configuration. Note that this means the processors each consume multiple Node IDs in order to identify their internal caching, home, and configuration agents.

PBSP Selection and CSR Access

After the Reset signal to a processor has been de-asserted, each processor socket will determine which of the cores will become the processor boot strap processor (PBSP) for that socket. This takes place before any boot firmware runs because the connection to the boot firmware storage device has not been established yet. Generally speaking, this task is performed by specialized microcode contained within the processor itself.

Control and Status Registers (CSRs) are the "knobs" that the boot firmware can set or examine in order to complete the task of bringing up the system. These CSRs are mapped into PCI Express™ (PCIe™) configuration space in a manner that is implementation-dependent, but the end result is that the PBSP will be able to perform read and write accesses to these CSRs both within the local socket and within remote sockets such as another processor or an IOH.

Firmware Discovery

The final step before boot firmware execution can begin is to finish establishing the path to the boot code storage device. In the topology shown in Figure 4.1, each processor socket sends the code fetch commands down the Intel QPI link connected to the IOH. Since there is only one IOH in this case, it is the LIOH. In Figure 4.2 the issue is a little more complex: the commands must be sent only to the LIOH. The problem is how to establish this path in the Intel QPI Link boot mode where no software is able to execute and help out this process.

The solution lies again in the LEP values sent out by each device, and in specialized hardware and microcode functions in the processor sockets. An *Agent Type* field is communicated as part of the LEP information. One possible Agent Type is a *Firmware Agent.* Only the LIOH will identify itself as the Firmware Agent during the LEP process. Which IOH is actually the LIOH is determined by hardware strapping on the printed circuit board.

The processor hardware and microcode therefore have the information needed to determine which physical link actually goes directly to the LIOH. The processor uses this information to configure itself to be able to send the boot firmware code fetches down that Intel QPI link connected to the LIOH. The LIOH in turn performs the actions necessary to actually interact with the boot code storage device and return the instructions back to the processor(s). At this point, the LIOH will only return the opcode back on the same Intel QPI link on which the request was received.

Handing Over Control

Once all of these processes are complete, control is handed over to the boot firmware at the reset vector. Everything necessary for basic Intel QPI code fetches has been established. Links have trained and are in the L0 operational state. LEP parameters have been captured and are used for initial setup and they also contain information useful for later configuration. Node IDs, routing paths to the LIOH, local and remote CSR access, and rudimentary address decoding initialization have all taken place. Note that each PBSP will begin executing the same code at this point. In Figure 4.1 topology, this means two cores will be executing. In Figure 4.2 topology there are also only two cores executing since only the sockets directly connected to the LIOH can become PBSPs. What happens next is a function of how the boot firmware is written. We shall examine those tasks in the next section.

Initial Boot Firmware Actions

The next step in the boot process is where the actual boot firmware code is fetched from the boot device and then control is turned over to that code. This firmware has many responsibilities outside of initializing the Intel QPI fabric. Getting the processor itself configured in terms of basic housekeeping, stacks, and memory ranges to use are all important issues that are beyond the scope of this text. Since these issues are not unique to platforms based on Intel QPI technology, we will not dwell on them. Suffice it to say that at this time we have the PBSPs able to execute code, access local and remote CSRs, and access an area of memory that can be used for read/write purposes. At this point the system is not running out of main system memory, but typically would utilize the cache memory within the processor itself for that purpose. This capability is sometimes referred to as Cache as Ram (CaR). This does not yet involve using the system-wide cache coherence mechanisms. This mode has a limitation in that only a single thread can run and nothing will be evicted from the cache. One of the first tasks of the boot firmware then is to decide which core will be the one allowed to execute instructions and access any read/write memory areas

System Bootstrap Processor (SBSP) Selection

This task is to decide which core from all of the available PSBPs will become the system bootstrap processor (SBSP). All cores other than the PSBPs will remain in a wait loop, or a low-power halt state, waiting for a wakeup message sent by the SBSP. Only the selected PBSP will go on to the next steps and become the SBSP.

Selection of the SBSP can be done in several implementation-dependant manners. One way is to rely upon the existence of special "read and increment" registers within a processor or an IOH. This type of register has the special property that the register will increment every time a read access is performed to it. In the case of SBSP selection, each PBSP will execute a read cycle to one of these registers, and they all must access the same physical register. The first one to perform that read will get a value of zero since the register was cleared during reset. The other PBSPs will get a nonzero value. The PBSP getting the zero value "wins" and is therefore declared the SBSP, which will execute the next portions of the boot firmware in a single threaded fashion. Other forms of semaphore operations to perform this selection process are also possible.

Early Link Actions

In order for the system to reach this point in the initialization process, the Intel QPI link pair between at least one processor socket (containing the core that becomes the SBSP) and the LIOH must be operational. The possibility remains that other link pairs may not be in the operational state. This could be because a socket is not populated, or because some hardware fault exists. It could also be that the platform design does not automatically initialize all links, but relies upon the boot firmware to complete that process. In those cases the SBSP has the responsibility to initiate the activation of the additional links.

Boot firmware has access to several pieces of information to help the firmware determine which links are present and operational. The first of these are the CSRs for the physical and link layers of each Intel QPI port. Configuration register accesses can be used by the SBSP to determine which links have reached the operational state. The second key pieces of information are the LEP values, which can also be examined through the use of configuration register accesses. The fact that valid LEP values exist indicates the link pair is operational. They also identify what type or agents exist and how they are connected to each other. This information will be vital to the later process of topology discovery and configuration.

Running Configuration Cycles

Prior to the SBSP being selected, hardware initialization already has certain conventions for accessing CSRs in both the SBSP's local socket and the CSRs for devices in other sockets. Since the boot firmware is generally written with at least some knowledge of the platform type on which the firmware is executed, specific address ranges are known to be the pointers to either local or remote CSRs. Accesses to the appropriate ranges will therefore get converted by the device's system interface logic into the Intel QPI transactions that cause read or write accesses to the desired registers. Note that at this point only non-coherent transactions are being used since the system memory and related resources have not yet been configured to enable full coherent operation. Since the SBSP is the only code thread executing at this point, and no data is being cached, this is not a problem.

Link Layer Configuration

While the link layer performs a default initialization when it comes up out of reset, the boot firmware may desire to alter the operating characteristics from their default values. The specifics of this process depend on the characteristics of each unique component and the target platform requirements, but the following items are representative of what would need to be configured.

Credit Allocation

As discussed in Chapter 3, flow control between the two connected link layers is performed through the use of a credit mechanism. The number of credits available is determined by the design of the receiver's hardware. A component design may also allow the boot firmware to alter how those total buffer resources are allocated into different virtual network credit pools. Platform requirements, such as workstation versus server application, may dictate a different assignment of these credits.

As an example, suppose an IOH device has a total incoming buffer space of 128 flits of storage available to it. The boot firmware can make assignments that distribute that total resource across all the message classes and virtual networks. One choice would be to assign one credit to each of the six message classes (MCs) in VN0, and a similar single credit to each MC in VN1. Because of the differing number of flits required to store the maximum sized packet in each MC, the total number of flits required for this VN0/VN1 allocation would be 54. See Table 4.1 for how this total is derived. Since 128 total flits are available, we can assign the remaining 74 flits to the VNA virtual network where the buffers can be shared on a flit basis by all MCs.

The application of these new credit allocations requires that they first be loaded into the appropriate CSRs, and then a firmware initiated link layer reset is performed. The new values will be "sticky" through the reset and will take effect when the link comes back up. Note that this reset would only be performed after all other link layer configuration settings are changed.

Table 4.1   Possible IOH Credit Allocation

Message Class	Flits per Credit	Credit Allocation (Assume 1 to each of VN0 and VN1)	Total Flit Buffers Required
NCS	3	2	6
NCB	11	2	22
NDR	1	2	2
DRS	11	2	22
SNP	1	2	2
HOM	0	0	0
Total of VN0 and VN1			54
All MCs in VNA	1	74	74

Note: Table assumes 128 total flits are available to be allocated. Since IOH devices do not receive HOM messages, no allocation is needed for that MC.

Power Management Configuration

The ability to use the link low-power states L0 and L1 is turned off by default. Since this is not a required feature, all components may not support these states. The LEP parameters do capture whether a device is capable of supporting either or both of these states, but it is up to the boot firmware to actually enable the function. The setting of specific bits in the link layer CSRs, at both ends of the link, is required to enable the ability to use the low-power states. Once these are set, the link layer is reset in order for these to take effect. Once initialized, no further runtime software intervention is required. Note that low-power states are not supported while in the slow mode of link operation. So while the ability to use the states may be enabled, the link layer is designed not to enter the low-power state while running at the slow mode transfer rates.

Recovering from Errors

Intel QPI devices provide a wealth of status and control information. They also have the ability to control the reset of various layers of the interface independently. Taken together, these give the boot firmware the option of taking additional measures if the status bits indicate the link initialization was not successful. While not required or implemented by all boot firmware developers, these capabilities do allow the platform developer some choices in how aggressive they wish to be in terms of bringing up the platform even in the presence of unexpected events.

One example is the failure of a physical layer to reach L0. After a timeout duration has elapsed, the boot firmware can issue a reset to the physical layer in question. If the error is transient, the link trains properly after the reset and the boot process can continue. Care must be taken when forcing a reset of any layer above the physical layer, especially if the link in question is part of the path that the boot firmware requires to continue executing its own code.

Topology Discovery and Configuration

Topology discovery is the task of finding out what agents are out there and how they are connected together. This is one of the prime functions of the SBSP since configuration of many remaining resources is dependent upon this discovery process. Configuring the routing tables that direct traffic on the links and setting up address decoders which determine the mapping from an address to a Node ID as well as delivery of information within a Node ID, are structures critical to the proper operation of the system. This section describes how this discovery process takes place and what specific structures are configured.

Example Topologies

The following sections discuss the topology discovery issues that can arise in several common platform configurations.

Single Processor Socket System

This is mentioned here to point out that in some cases the topology discovery may be trivial. In such systems there is only one processor socket and a single IOH device. One Intel QPI link pair connects the two together. As this is the only possible configuration in this case, the processor hardware may in fact have initialized all relevant hardware resources. If either of the devices is not present, the system is nonfunctional so no configuration needs to be (or even can be) performed.

Dual Processor Socket System

These systems are represented by Figure 4.1. Topology determination starts becoming more interesting since more options are possible in these systems. One of the processor sockets must be populated and functional, but we do not have advance information about which socket that will be. In the Intel QPI link boot mode, the LIOH must also be populated and at least partially functional. All of the link-pairs may not be operational and this may at least impair platform functionality. The capabilities of the processor need consideration. For example, if route-through functionality is not supported then all links must be operational for the system to work when both processor sockets are populated. Route-through is the ability of a device's system interface logic to receive an incoming Intel QPI packet and then route the packet through to the final destination if that destination differs from the current socket's Node ID. If route-through is supported, then the boot firmware may be able to make allowances to get the system up and running even if one of the processor-to-IOH links was not operational. Note that support of such features is a product-specific choice. Typically the IOH does not support route-through. Processors intended for the small-scale two-socket systems typically do not support route-through either. For the purposes of this text, we shall assume that route-through is not supported by devices used in these platforms. In a typical two socket platform, the only configuration choice therefore is whether or not both processor sockets are populated. At a minimum one processor and the LIOH must be present.

Four Processor Socket System

Figure 4.2 shows a possible four processor, dual IOH configuration. Topology discovery in these systems becomes more interesting. Processors for such systems typically do support route-through and in fact they must support route-through in order to support the configuration shown. There may also be anywhere from one to four processors populated, plus one or two IOHs of which one must be the LIOH. Furthermore, the individual link pairs may or not be operational, or in fact may not be physically present. As such, this topology discussion is the basis for much of what follows.

Discovery Process

These sections describe the basic process for discovery of what devices and links are operational in two particular platform configurations. The single processor system will not be discussed.

Dual Processor Socket System

In this system, the LIOH and one processor have to be functional, otherwise there is no way to execute the boot firmware. Since the only choice is whether or not the second processor socket is populated, there is a simple process for determining that information. Processors contain a specific Vendor ID information register. The SBSP will read that register from the other processor and if the correct value is not found, that socket is assumed to be empty or at least nonfunctional. This approach is sufficient although more aggressive boot firmware approaches may attempt to further isolate the problem by examining link status registers on the local or even the remote socket. If the correct value is found, then the SBSP knows that the processor exists and that the link to that processor is working. The SBSP will now have identified the quantity and Node IDs of processors and the IOHs in the system. This information is used for configuring those resources more fully later on.

Four Processor Socket System

Here the system configuration is much less constrained and the simple method described above would not work for the more general cases. What can be used are the LEP values captured during the link layer initialization process. Recall that the LEP values record the sender's port number, Node ID information, and the type(s) of agent contained in the sending device. The SBSP can use this information to start building a table of connectivity information, starting with what is connected to its own socket and then working outward to discover what is connected to the remote sockets. Eventually a conceptual map can be created that identifies all of the working links and the interconnected devices.

The discovery of all components in the system is usually carried out in Breadth-First-Order approach. This is used to minimize the path length from the SBSP to any other component as well as to minimize the routing spans. Figure 4.3 depicts this approach. The SBSP discovers its neighbor (one hop away, or directly connected by an Intel QuickPath Interconnect link) components first by reading the LEP of each enabled port, then discovers the neighbor's neighbors (two hops away), and so on. This discovery process continues recursively until all the components in the system have been identified. The topology information collected during the discovery process is implementation-specific, but at the minimum it should contain the following: Socket ID, Agent Type, Enabled Ports, List of {Neighbor Components, Port from itself to the Neighbor, Port from the Neighbor to itself} of each socket in the system.

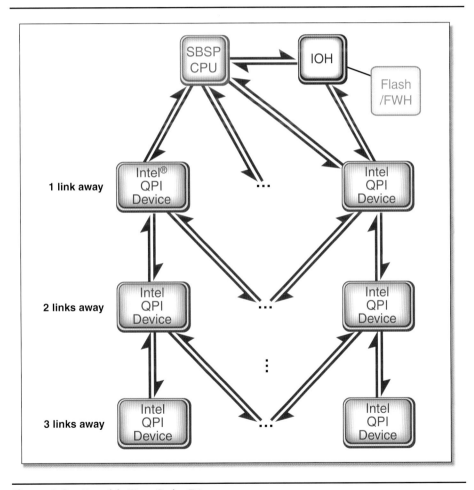

Figure 4.3   Breadth-First-Order Discovery

Once the discovery process has collected the LEP-based information, a communication infrastructure can be built between the SBSP and all other devices (targets). This communication infrastructure enables the targets to respond correctly to transactions originated by the SBSP, such as read/write requests to target CSRs. The communication infrastructure between the SBSP and its neighbors is set first. For the direct neighbors (Target), the infrastructure consists of the minimal set of *routing table array* (RTA) entries both on SBSP and the target components. For components that are N hops away (where N > 1), the infrastructure requires the setting of the RTAs for the links between targets that are N–1 hops away from the SBSP and their neighbors that are N hops away from the SBSP. The end result is that the SBSP is able to access any target more than one hop away in distance.

Communication Infrastructure Programming

The Intel QPI communication infrastructure consists of the minimal set of RTA entries that enables the SBSP to communicate freely with all other Intel QPI components in the system. The previous step of discovery and this step of configuration are executed in an alternating fashion, discovery of a device, programming the fabric, discovering more devices, and so on. The information needed to build this fabric includes the Socket ID, Agent Type, local port to parent device, and parent device port to local port. With this information, the SBSP can program the structures of the routing layer so that Intel QPI transactions can be delivered to their intended destination.

In the two socket platform configuration shown in Figure 4.1, the only routing decision to be made is where the IOH device should go when the IOH needs to send or receive information from main memory. This assumes that the processors in this platform do not support route-through. This also requires that the processor itself is aware of the system configuration and will automatically perform any required RTA setup so that transactions generated by the processor itself are directed to the proper target.

In the four socket platform shown in Figure 4.2, the RTA setup depends upon what was discovered during the earlier process. Certain sockets may not be populated or links may not exist or be functional. While there is a great deal of flexibility in how the routing paths are configured, there are also some limitations that apply. One such limitation, at least in the first product implementations of Intel QPI, is that there must be only one path between any two agents. In other words, adaptive routing based on some real-time conditions is not supported by those implementations. A major goal of the routing choices is to minimize the number of hops between all endpoints. Paths from one device to another can differ from the return path in order to perform load balancing on the Intel QPI links in the platform. Care must be taken in ring type configurations in order to prevent system deadlocks. Routing around the ring is recommended. One other obvious restriction is that devices that do not support route-through (like the IOH) can only be endpoints and must not be part of the path between two devices.

In both platform configurations, the routing layer RTAs are programmed by the SBSP by performing CSR writes to the appropriate registers. Note that the exact format may vary from one device to the next depending on the flexibility each specific device provides in its routing layer implementation. While the discovery and programming of this information may seem to be complicated if the topology is unknown, in practice the task of the boot firmware developer is simplified because some knowledge of the intended platform configurations is taken into account.

Full Speed Link Transition

As we have mentioned previously, Intel QPI links come up by default in a slow mode. For maximum system performance, the links are transitioned to an operational speed. The exact speed used depends upon the specific hardware device and platform configuration, but both ends of the link are told what that speed will be; there is currently no automatic negotiation process used. Exactly when in the boot process this transition takes place is up to the discretion of the firmware developer.

Setting full speed operation involves changing the clocking ratios inside each device, programming the platform-specific link equalization settings, setting any other physical layer controls, and then issuing a reset to the physical layer. The link will then retrain at the selected operational speed.

Link equalization settings are described in Chapter 3. They shape the outgoing waveform depending on the needs of the link on that platform type. Boot firmware does not determine the correct values for these tap settings. That is a hardware design and analysis task that yields specific numbers that the boot firmware will then load into the appropriate control registers.

The number of taps and their resolution (number of bits per tap) is determined by the component design. The boot firmware in this case simply picks up the values from a known location in the boot code and puts them into the hardware.

The SBSP has the responsibility to check for maximum supported speed of the devices installed in the platform. This information generally is conveyed through hardware strap settings on the platform. Care must be taken to ensure that all devices operate within the speed limitations of the platform. Once the operational speed is chosen, CSRs in each device are used to specify the appropriate clocking ratios. Note that Intel QPI devices do not have the concept of a fixed gear ratio where the processor's internal clock is tied in some way to the speed of the Intel QPI links. This was the case in FSB systems but does not apply to Intel QPI platforms.

An additional step in the move to full-speed operation is to enable specific physical layer features such as scrambling and retraining as they are required by a particular platform. Full-speed link operation, with retraining, scrambling, and equalization in effect, takes place after the reset is performed and the physical layers retrain up to the L0 state. Once the links transition to full-speed operation, they cannot return to the slow mode without a Power-Good reset.

Higher Layer Initialization

Initialization to this point has basically established the ability for the SBSP to communicate with all other devices, but the type of transactions being used is limited to the non-coherent type. Configuration registers can be examined and set, but real system memory operation is not in the picture yet. Furthermore, the ability to turn on the various caching structures throughout the system has not been enabled. These more complex transactions are vital to the routine operation of the operating system. The preparation for these functions primarily involves the setting of coherent protocol related CSRs, the establishment of various lists, the discovery and configuration of the main system memory, and the setup of various address decoding structures. This section discusses the first two topics, which are most closely related to the Intel QPI fabric itself. The memory and address decode related topics are discussed in the following section.

Coherent Transaction Snooping Modes

Components that contain caching agents and home agents identify themselves to the SBSP through the LEP process. Caching agents are those that initiate read and write requests into the main memory space. Since they can keep copies of memory data in their own internal caches, they must be configured to participate in the system coherency scheme. Home agents in turn are the agents to which those read and write requests are directed. Every unit of memory (a 64-byte cache line) has one and only one home agent responsible for that cache line-sized chunk of memory. All caching agents and home agents must be configured so that they are aware of and configured consistently with respect to each other.

Smaller-scale systems as in Figure 4.1 may have most of the choices preconfigured or determined by the hardware design. More complex systems allow additional flexibility requiring specific configuration steps.

Depending upon the implementation, there may be several options as to how the snooping or coherency resolution process is handled. The two basic modes are source-issued snoops and home-issued snoops. In source snooping, the caching agent generating the request (the source of the transaction) is responsible for sending all required snoops for that transaction. This typically involves the use of a peer agent list, which is essentially a bitmap of Node IDs that defines to the caching agent the Node IDs of all other peer agents that must be snooped. The SBSP typically determines this bitmap for each caching agent and programs this peer agent list of Node IDs into the appropriate CSR.

Home-issued snooping requires that the home agent that receives the read or write request be the agent that generates any required snoops. In this case each home agent is configured with a bitmap that identifies all of the caching agents that might need to be snooped. In turn each caching agent is configured so that they do not generate any snoops when they issue a request. This could be done by simply setting the peer agent list bitmap to be empty or null. It could also be based on the way in which the hardware is designed and not require any specific configuration.

However the snooping process is handled by the particular platform, it is the responsibility of the SBSP to ensure that all CSRs related to the snooping operation are programmed correctly.

Transaction Pool Allocations

Because the Intel QuickPath Interconnect fabric relies upon pre-allocation of resources, a finite number of outstanding transactions can exist at any one time. Transaction ID bits are used in every transaction to help uniquely define what is taking place at any one point in time. The number of bits defined is finite. Hardware is therefore designed so that the IDs will not be reused until a particular transaction sequence is completely retired. Home agents are designed to accept all transactions sent to them so it is important that the number of possible transactions be limited to the capacity of the home agent hardware. The structure that manages the outstanding transactions at the home agent is known as the *Tracker*. The total number of outstanding transactions that can be issued by a single caching agent is termed *MaxRequests*. Home agents and caching agents must be configured to share these limited resources and make certain that the maximum limits are not exceeded.

This configuration depends upon the topology discovered earlier. A system with a larger number of agents will have to be careful and assign a smaller number of available transactions per agent. A smaller system may be able to dedicate more transactions per agent. Devices designed for larger-scale platforms have more available resources and more flexibility in how those resources are allocated. This gives the platform developer the freedom to tune the hardware capabilities to match the intended application.

Interrupt Configuration

In the typical platform configurations shown in Figure 4.1 and 4.2, the IOH component has the ability to generate interrupts on the Intel QPI fabric for a wide variety of reasons. In this type of platform, all interrupts "south" of the IOH must go up through the IOH and then will get converted to Virtual Legacy Wire (VLW) messages on the Intel QPI links to the processors. VLW messages are used because there are no dedicated interrupt pins on the processor; interrupts flow as messages across the Intel QPI link. Some examples include:

- Interrupt requests from the ICH such as NMI, SMI, INTR
- Error conditions detected by the IOH

In addition, the platform design may dictate that certain events get handled in a particular manner. For example, the assertion of the NMI pin may need to get routed to generate an MCA interrupt.

The IOH (or other such device with interrupt ability) will contain CSRs that control how these interrupt functions are handled. There will also be CSRs which control the ultimate destination of those interrupts.

Processor devices may also need to be configured with the target for *IntAck* messages to be sent to the I/O proxy containing the 8259A equivalent interrupt controller. They also may send *IntPrioUpd* messages to other devices, so a list of those may get configured.

Broadcast Lists

Broadcast transactions are those that are sent to multiple final destinations. These could go to all processors, or all IOH devices, for example. Since Intel QPI transactions are inherently point-to-point, broadcast transactions are actually accomplished by sending multiple point-to-point transactions, each one targeted to a unique destination. For this to work, a list of where to send specific transactions must be configured. There are several types of broadcast transactions to be concerned with.

Interrupt List

Since all interrupts are actually sent as messages over the Intel QPI fabric, specific interrupt functions are mapped into messages that contain fields that identify the type of interrupt. For SMI, NMI, MCI, and INIT interrupts there is a bitmap configured in the hardware of all devices able to generate these interrupts. That bitmap defines which agents to send the interrupt messages to. By default these are sent to all processor agents.

Non-Coherent Broadcast List

Certain transaction types are used for power management and Virtual Legacy Wire (VLW) traffic. Since these may need to go to multiple destinations, a bitmap is configured with the appropriate Node IDs.

Quiesce Broadcast List

Certain transaction flows are used in the quiescing of system activity. This list is used to coordinate the locking and Quiesce flows with the Lock Arbiter. Two lists are used, one for processors and one for IOHs. Each list is programmed with valid Node IDs for either the processors or IOHs respectively.

Preparing for the Operating System

Now that a communication framework has been established, the time has come to finish preparing all of the remaining resources required to be able to turn control over from the single SBSP running the boot firmware to the operating system running on all available processors and I/O devices.

Processor Readiness

Prior to beginning the initialization of main system memory, several system conditions must be met. First is that the SBSP has been selected and that all other processors have been designated as APs and are in some sort of wait for interrupt process. Any microcode updates have been completed at this point. Cache memory may be configured to be used as read/write storage by the SBSP, with no other accesses that could cause evictions. The SBSP will also be aware of certain platform operating characteristics such as the core and Intel QPI link operating frequencies. This will help in the computation of various timing parameters used in this process. The SBSP is then ready to begin dealing with the system memory controllers.

At this point the minimum set of system address decoders have been configured to the point of allowing CSR access by the SBSP to all other devices. They also are able to support non-coherent reads and writes directed towards memory regions, even if those regions are not known to exist yet. This is sufficient to allow the SBSP to perform the memory initialization. Later on however, the address decoding structures will be more completely configured to take into account the full system memory abilities.

Memory Configuration

The use of multiple integrated memory controllers within the processor hardware is a key characteristic of many systems using Intel QPI technology. While the specific memory technology and number of memory interfaces can vary from one processor design to the next, the connection of a memory system to each of the processor sockets is almost always the case in Intel QPI platforms. The actual characteristics of the memory at each socket are usually discovered when the system goes through the boot process, and the memory system must be prepared for use. While this process shares many characteristics in common with previous generation platforms, systems based on Intel QPI technology have the ability to utilize memory that may exist at multiple locations. This requires some additional initialization steps that were not part of previous system designs.

Memory Population Rules

Memory controllers in general cannot support any arbitrary population of DIMM devices. While the details are platform-specific, there are some guidelines that can be mentioned here. The key point is that the code executing on the SBSP may not be designed to handle all conceivable populations; boot firmware will assume some constraints have been followed. Here are some of the typical population constraints.

- Mixing of RDIMMs and UDIMMs is not supported
- Mixing DIMMS with different timings will result in supporting only the fastest timing supported by all
- DIMMS of differing geometry, size, or speed can be mixed within a channel
- Use of RAS features such as mirroring and sparing will require matching DIMMs across applicable channels

Detect Installed DIMM Configuration

The SBSP at this point can go out through the processor's SMBus interface and access the Serial Presence Detect (SPD) data on all possible DIMM slots. This allows the SBSP to enforce any DIMM population rules that are required by that platform type. The SBSP also detects any nodes with unpopulated DIMM slots that are then disabled. Information on the memory size for each rank, channel, and socket is saved for later use.

Establish Memory-specific Values

Once the SPD data has been collected, the SBSP has the information needed to compute appropriate values and then configure the memory controller hardware to match the electrical and timing characteristics of the installed DIMMs. The details of this operation will vary from one platform type to the next, depending on the type of memory supported. For example, DDR3 memory controllers will require different steps than a memory controller designed for buffered DIMM channels. A warm reset will be required later to switch to the newly programmed values.

DIMM Initialization

The next step is to bring the actual DIMM devices out of reset. Previously only the SPD information has been accessed, it is now time to enable access to the DRAM arrays. This step is highly dependent on the memory technology used and on the specific functions of the memory controller itself. For our purposes it is sufficient to note that the SBSP performs a series of CSR accesses to the memory controllers and that the memory should be functional once this step is completed.

Conduct Memory Test

The memory controller hardware typically contains functions that facilitate performing a test of the memory arrays. This hardware includes the ability to generate data patterns and to write those to multiple DIMM devices in parallel. Errors are detected and logged and, depending on the features of the memory controller, bad devices are mapped out so that the boot process can continue. The SBSP uses this hardware capability to conduct the test and then to take corrective actions as needed based on the results. This test is run twice. The first pass tests the memory and maps out bad locations. The second pass is used to initialize the Error Check and Correct (ECC) information stored in the DIMMs.

After Self-Test

Upon completion of the memory test, any remaining housekeeping functions of the memory controller can be attended to. Any unused portions of the hardware may be turned off to save power. All remaining host timing parameters are programmed. Patrol scrubbing and thermal throttling hardware can be enabled and any RAS modes such as DIMM sparing or memory mirroring can commence.

At this point the SBSP also has enough information to have a complete picture of the available system memory resources. The SBSP knows the memory size on each local node and therefore the total system memory. It also has information on any failed DIMMs. This information is used to finish setting up system-wide address decoding resources.

Address Decoding

Once the full system topology is known, including all available memory resources, the full system address space can be mapped onto the available devices depending on their resource needs. All of the various architecturally defined address regions such as Flash, DRAM_LO, DRAM_HI, Local Config, Global CSRs, MMIOL, MMIOH, and PCIe need to be defined in a consistent manner across the distributed devices.

On previous generation FSB-based platforms, the processor and I/O devices could simply direct all memory and I/O traffic to the North Bridge controller. The location desired was specified by the address of the transaction. This worked in part because all system memory was controlled through the North Bridge. Systems based on Intel QuickPath Interconnect technology typically contain multiple memory controllers distributed throughout the platform. Transactions being inserted into the Intel QPI fabric need a method by which their ultimate destination is defined in terms of a Node ID. The structure that performs this function is known as the *source address decoder* (SAD). SADS are part of the hardware that helps form the information that goes into the outgoing Intel QPI packet. A lookup process is used by the device at the source of the request. This process takes the intended address, plus other attributes of the transaction, and goes into a lookup table that generates the Node ID for that address. Figure 4.4 is a representation of the SAD function.

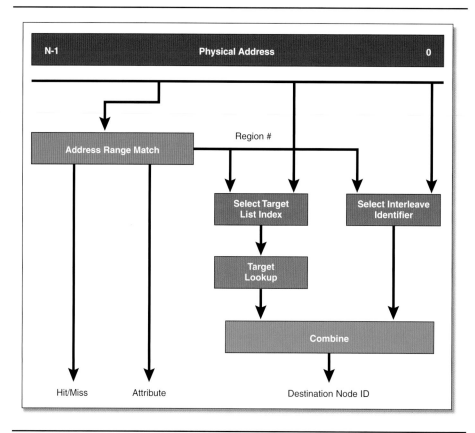

Figure 4.4 Block Diagram of Source Address Decoder Function

In a similar manner, a complementary structure known as the *target address decoder* (TAD) exists at every Intel QPI agent that can receive transactions. This structure accepts transactions sent to its Node ID and then routes them to the appropriate functional block within the component.

In simple configurations, the SAD and TAD setup may be done almost completely by hardware. This is possible because of limited system topologies with limited numbers of devices and therefore limited Node IDs. However, more complex systems require boot firmware configuration in order to properly initialize these structures. Full configuration of the SADs and TADs in a system typically takes place after system memory initialization has been completed.

SAD Programming

SAD register structure varies by component depending on the level of address mapping flexibility the device is designed to support. A typical processor will have multiple SAD registers. Each register takes in specific portions of the address bits as an index into an array that is programmed to define the Node ID for that address range and transaction type. Multiple SAD registers are programmed to define or "claim" the various memory regions as mentioned above. Different SADs may have differing abilities in terms of the size of the memory region that they control. The content of all SAD registers system wide must be consistent relative to each other. In other words, a given address always maps to the same Node ID.

Several levels of programming are needed to initialize the system memory map.

1. SAD registers in the IOHs and each processor are programmed

2. System Address Gap (SAG) registers are programmed for each memory controller channel. System memory address gaps may occur when multiple memory channels are populated in uneven patterns, potentially creating gaps in the total address space. SAG registers allow those gaps to be removed so that the memory is perceived as one contiguous space for each memory channel.

3. Memory controller rank limit and way registers are programmed for each rank

Since the SAD structure specifies a Destination Node ID, SADs can be programmed to facilitate *socket interleaving* of memory accesses based on a very flexible range of addressing choices. For example, alternating cache line–sized accesses could go to different sockets. Likewise an entire range of cache lines could be sent into one socket with another consecutive range targeted to a different socket.

TAD Programming

TAD structures are used to decode the particular internal function that is the ultimate destination of an incoming transaction. A typical application is to define the particular portion of the memory controller that will handle a particular read or write request sent to the Node ID containing that memory.

TADs also exist in other areas since a single Node ID may cover multiple functions within a socket. In those cases the TAD structure may be pre-determined by the hardware design and the targeting will be based on information contained within the incoming message. The most interesting TADs from a programming and system configuration perspective are those that are associated with the memory controllers.

In a processor with multiple memory controllers, and possibly multiple memory channels per memory controller, the TADs can be used to route the incoming transaction to a particular memory channel. This allows for *channel interleaving* which involves intra-socket routing. Recall that the SAD allowed for *socket interleaving* where transactions are destined for different sockets. Taken together the combination of SAD and TAD structures gives the boot firmware a great deal of flexibility in how to balance memory transactions across all of the available memory.

Memory Interleaving Examples

Memory interleaving is a process by which memory on a cache line–sized granularity is stored in a noncontiguous form. The advantages of doing this include bandwidth improvements because multiple memory transactions can take place in parallel. Another advantage is the reduction of thermal hotspots because memory accesses can be spread out over a wider physical area. While these advantages do exist, it is worth noting that there is no perfect solution for all systems in terms of interleaving. Some operating systems are Non-Uniform Memory Access (NUMA) aware and are capable of dealing with multiple distributed memory regions. Other OS implementations may not be. The hardware design using SAD and TAD structures gives the platform developer the choice of whether to use interleaving and, if implemented, how to use interleaving to best meet their needs.

Figure 4.5 gives a representation of how socket-level interleaving would work across two sockets. Alternating cache line accesses to memory are directed to either the left or right memory controller. Consecutive memory accesses would therefore occupy both memory controllers and not place the burden solely upon one of them.

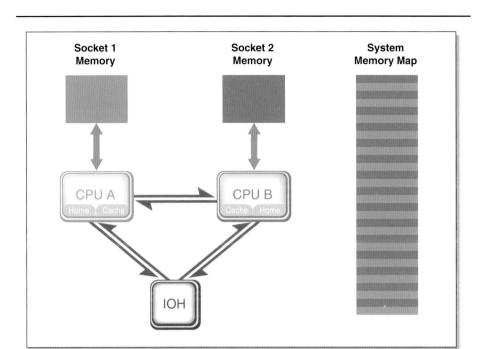

Figure 4.5 Cache Line Interleave Across Two Sockets

Figure 4.6 shows a more complex example. In this case the memory space is divided into six regions, two sockets with three memory channels per socket. The SAD controls directing traffic to the socket, while the TAD programming directs traffic to the particular memory channel within the socket. Consecutive memory accesses in this case would occupy all memory channels across the platform.

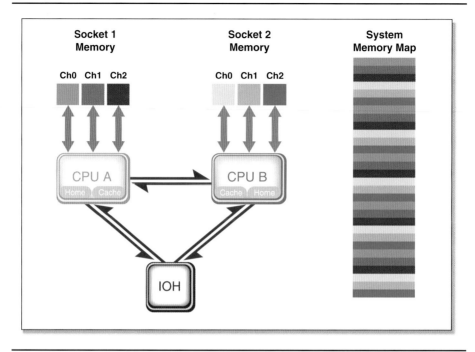

Figure 4.6   Socket and Channel Interleaving

Additional Functional and RAS Modes

Various functional and RAS-related features may be supported on a given platform design. Even if a feature is supported by the hardware, the overall platform architecture choice may be to not use that feature. These capabilities usually are configured prior to turning over control to the next level of software.

One feature defined by Intel QPI that may or may not be used is the Viral indication. Protocol level CSRs in the devices can be used to turn this on or off at boot time. A similar situation exists for handling of the Poison bit that is defined for some type of packets. Please see Chapter 5 for more information on the Viral and Poison indicators.

Another common configuration area is the logic that controls the link level retry process. For example, CSRs can be used to determine how many times the link layer should reinitialize the physical layer when attempting to recover from severe link problems.

These are a few notable examples of configuration options related to Intel QPI. The devices themselves typically contain a set of other choices that usually are configured before running higher-level software. Consult the specific product's documentation for details in these areas.

Hand-off to the Operating System

At this point, the functions required to initialize the capabilities related to Intel QuickPath Interconnect will have been completed. From this point on, the fabric performs its tasks without any intervention or control from software. Of course if the system configuration changes, portions of the above process will need to be repeated. The rest of the platform's operating system boot process would proceed in a manner that is similar to previous generation platforms. All processors will eventually be started up, and the OS load and execute steps can proceed without requiring any direct knowledge of the underlying fabric.

Summary

This chapter has covered the process of getting the myriad of hardware resources properly initialized so that real work can then be performed by the system. The interaction of boot firmware with the hardware was discussed, beginning with the basic steps of getting links operational and proceeding through memory initialization. The next chapter explores some of the higher-level capabilities of systems based on the Intel QuickPath Architecture.

Chapter 5

Advanced System Considerations

Any sufficiently advanced technology is indistinguishable from magic
— Arthur C. Clarke

This chapter describes complex system characteristics and the way in which the infrastructure of the Intel® QuickPath Architecture allows for systems to be developed with these high-end feature sets. These complex features include dynamic system reconfiguration, partitioning, increasing the memory subsystem availability, and bringing links on line and off.

The collection of mechanisms that configure and control the operation of system based on an Intel QPI topology is the system management infrastructure. It can comprise two distinct subcomponents, in-band and out-of-band system management. The out-of-band system management infrastructure consists of the service processors that operate in parallel to the main platform components. Service processors configure and control the operation of the platform through dedicated access interfaces to processor and chipset components such as SMBus and JTAG. These are distinct from the interfaces that the platform components use to communicate among themselves. The in-band system management infrastructure consists of platform firmware running on the processor that is used to configure and control the platform components by accessing the processor and chipset configuration and status registers (CSRs) over Intel QPI.

In addition, descriptions of power management, interrupt delivery and system management attributes are contained in the Intel QPI infrastructure. It should be noted that many of the features addressed in this section can be reliant on each other. Also, the examples used are merely examples and do not necessarily reflect any specific product implementation of the feature set or the only possible solution to implement the given feature.

Dynamic Reconfigurations

The architects of the Intel QuickPath Interconnect have created a comprehensive system architecture that goes beyond just defining the cache coherence protocol, link, and physical layers. In particular they have defined an infrastructure capable of addressing large platform requirements. One major area that should be addressed is to provide the hooks to support dynamic reconfiguration. Dynamic reconfiguration capabilities can be used to react to a component failure or to improve overall system utilization, performance, and power efficiency. For example, if a component fails, the system can be reconfigured to operate without that resource or to replace that resource. Alternatively, dynamic reconfiguration can be used to support static or dynamic hard partitions. This allows resources to be moved between partitions (dynamic or static), to better match hardware resources to application demand thus improving overall system utilization. Some of the resource management operations to support these usage models include Online Add/Online Delete/Online Remove (OL_A/OL_D/OL_R) of a field replaceable unit (FRU). These operations can include reconfiguring the routing tables, mapping out a failed link or the mapping out of a failed memory image of a platform, and so on.

Dynamic reconfiguration relies on the ability to access configuration registers (either in band or out of band), Quiesce/Dequiesce features, link initialization at anytime (not just at system reset or power up), the ability for the links to operate at different widths/speeds, and so forth.

Partitioning

A system based on Intel QPI links can support dynamic or static partitions where the links (or the system topology) are shared among the partitions. Fundamentally each partition is a set of resources that are functionally isolated from other partitions. In the case of a hard partition, each hard partition is electrically isolated from other hard partitions so that it is impossible for an error event in one hard partition to bring down another hard partition. In order to support hard partitioning on Intel QPI link boundaries, Intel QPI links can be forced to remain in a non-operational state where no traffic is passed between the components. In a typical "glueless" system topology (a topology without any node controller hardware components), each agent will have a unique Node ID (NID) and each partition a unique set of NIDs. When node controllers are used to build up a large scale system, the node controllers typically allow different partitions to use the same NID. In addition, Intel QPI agents can provide address decoder and routing capabilities so that reuse of the same NIDs is also possible even for a topology with no node controller components.

The system management agent, via in-band accesses (that is, over the Intel QPI fabric) or an out-of-band method, can configure the system address maps and routing tables of the individual nodes. (Reference the System Management section for a complete description of how a system management agent can be an Intel QPI configuration agent). With the ability to access the configuration registers distributed across all the nodes (where only a given set of node IDs is assigned to a given partition), the system topology as well as the system management agent can easily be shared between multiple partitions of the platform.

A key distinction between some types of logical partitioning (static or dynamic) versus virtual partitioning is that the system address maps for each logical partition has a "physical" address "0". On top of that logical partition a user can have multiple OS instances running in their own virtual spaces but there is physically only one address location 0, 1, 2, through "top of address space".

In addition there are many ways to partition. One could:

■ Partition at the socket or multi-socket granularity where each physical entity resides in one and only one partition. In this case partitions really only share the system interconnect and in the case of hard partitions, these can be isolated from each other.

■ Partition at the subcomponent granularity (sometimes referred to as firm partitioning). In this mode the subcomponent possesses enough hardware to logically act as two or more unique entities. Examples of these entities are:

– Caching Agent where one or more cores reside behind it.

– Set of PCI Express™ (PCIe™) ports in an I/O hub (IOH).

  One very simple way to partition at the subcomponent level is with Node IDs. As an example, if a processor socket containing four cores supports subcomponent partitioning at core granularity, then each core and associated resources are assigned a unique set of Node IDs.

These aspects of partitioning are beyond the scope of this book. Many papers and books have already been dedicated to this level of partitioning.

Static Partitioning

For this book partitioning is always assumed to be dynamic, unless otherwise stated. The partitioning is dynamic if resources can be added or removed from a partition without the need to reboot the system or the affected partitions. With static partitioning, the system is partitioned at boot time and repartitioning requires a reboot of the affected partitions. Static partitioning can then be thought of as the "simplest" case of dynamic partitioning.

  In static partitioning resources are configured at time "0" to be specifically tied to a given partition. The entire system is configured, resources allocated, the OS instances (or hypervisors) boot all at the same time.

Dynamic Partitioning

Dynamic partitioning requires many of the constructs described later in this chapter. To support dynamic partitioning a system should have the ability to:

■ Quiesce/Dequiesce the system and/or a set of links.

■ Reconfigure Route Tables, System address decoders of a system via a configuration interface.

■ De-allocate/Allocate physical memory or I/O interfaces.

When a system supports dynamic partitioning, it provides the user with the ability to reconfigure the system and to move resources between different partitions, commonly done at the field replacement unit (FRU) level. In serviceability terms, each FRU is the smallest piece of a system that can be replaced by a service technician in the field. Partitioning a system so that resources can replaced in the field only needs to be done to the FRU level, because pieces smaller than an FRU won't be replaced. FRUs could be what-ever size the particular platform decides upon: a DIMM, a power supply, or an entire populated motherboard. In addition to the requirements of the hardware to be reconfigured, online addition and deletion of a module from a running partition usually requires OS support as well. As stated earlier, a module may comprise processors only, memory (including the memory controller), an IOH (or a subcomponent of the IOH), or some combination of the preceding components depending on the particular implementation and system configuration. Multiple partitions can exist within a system, each of which is logically isolated from the other, providing different degrees of reliability and security depending on the particular requirements of the partitions.

Moving system resources (the modules) logically between the partitions using the system service processor (SSP) requires either an out-of-band interface (like SMBus or JTAG) or the Intel QPI in-band interface to a configuration agent.

Quiesce and Dequiesce

Intel QPI at the protocol layer provides mechanism to completely quiet a partition (or an entire system) to guarantee complete atomic operations by a system or configuration agent. This ability provides the environment for a system administrator to change a system's or partition's configurations. The Quiesce/Dequiesce feature can be utilized for

- General system monitoring by the system administrator – such as the dumping of error logs, performance monitoring, and so on.

- Onlining/offlining of a component in the topology.

- Moving system resources (memory, processors, I/O) to enable dynamic partitioning.

- Advanced memory features such as DIMM sparing, mirroring, and migration—specifically the reprogramming of system address and routing tables.

The Quiesce/Dequiesce flows are similar to the old atomic LOCK flows and completely suspend all new transactions from being issued except by the system configuration agent.

Note

> The system administrator cannot suspend protocol traffic over the Intel® QuickPath Interconnect topology indefinitely. The duration of the suspension should adhere to the time constraints of the running operating systems, the core transaction timeout restrictions, and so on.

A quiescence operation is initiated either by a particular core (in-band) or by the system service processor (referred to as SSP) via an out-of-band mechanism. The SSP can control the quiescence through its non-Intel QPI network or can designate an Intel QPI agent (like a specific core), which then initiates the in-band flow.

On Line Addition or Deletion (OL_*)

A key feature necessary to enable dynamic partitioning is the support for on-line addition and deletion (OL_*). With OL_*, a partition can be resized by adding and removing resources without the need to reboot the system or restart the affected partition. In addition, OL_* provides the ability to remove and add a field replaceable unit (FRU).

The OL_* sequences also contain several steps in the operating systems. A key requirement for any OL_* operation is for the ability of the system firmware to quiesce the domain of interest so that many system resources, such as routing tables and address decoders, can be updated in what essentially appears to be an atomic operation to the software layers above the firmware.

Additional Memory Subsystem Features

Similar to other link based systems, an Intel QPI-based system allows for a distributed memory subsystem or subsystems. Just as other platforms' memory subsystems provide some level of protection against memory failures, a system based on Intel QPI technology can (and almost always will) be designed to provide ECC or Intel Single Device Data Correction (SDDC) algorithms to provide protection against data loss. The ECC/Intel SDDC provides data recovery characteristics of a DIMM that is constructed from multiple DRAM components. These algorithms provide survivability from single bit or chip failures without any loss of data. Algorithms based on CRC/ECC combinations exist that can reconstruct correct data even when multiple devices on the DIMM are failing.

In addition to data protection, the memory system(s) can implement scrubbing logic. The purpose of this logic is to read every location in the memory subsystem looking for correctable errors and then correct those errors as part of the scrubbing process. This avoids a weak memory cell from degrading further to an uncorrectable event. ECC/Intel SDDC and scrubbing logic provides any memory subsystem with enhanced availability characteristics. Again any memory subsystem can provide this level of protection, because the logic/algorithms can be completely contained in the memory subsystem itself. These features provide a certain level of protection but there is a common link and that is the control logic of the memory subsystem itself. What protects the user's data from this type of failure?

In the event a system requires a robust memory subsystem with greater reliability and availability, Intel QPI provides an infrastructure that supports features such as DIMM sparing, memory mirroring, and memory migration.

DIMM Sparing

DIMM sparing is an availability feature similar to that of a spare tire of an automobile. In the event of a failing tire (it is always easier to change a tire that is going flat than one that has completely failed); the driver replaces the failing tire with the spare. This is exactly the usage model of DIMM Sparing. In the event that a DIMM is determined to be failing (and prior to data loss), the contents of the failing DIMM are copied to the spare so no down time is experienced by the end user.

General DIMM Sparing Usage Model

In general terms, as a platform is first being configured, at least one DIMM of a memory subsystem is logically set aside and does not appear in the system address map. This DIMM is the "spare tire" of the composite memory subsystem. The composite memory subsystem is the set of all memory controllers in the system. As a memory subsystem is servicing requests it is also refreshing the DRAM and potentially scrubbing the memory subsystem in the background. As correctable errors are detected, the memory content is "corrected" and written back into the DIMM. A certain number of correctable errors are expected for a DIMM.

There will come a point where:

■ The ratio of correctable single bit errors is too high for a given DIMM, indicating that a device is failing on that DIMM. An acceptable failure rate should include the aspects of environment (temperature, altitude, ventilation, and so on) and any rate above that is therefore deemed excessive (number of errors over a given time interval) signaling that this DIMM should be replaced.

- A device on a DIMM has completely failed and the memory subsystem is relying on the error recovery algorithm to recreate the data stored in the failed device. In this case a single soft error in another device could result in an uncorrectable error, and the correctable failure rate of the DIMM would be incredibly high (every access would most likely log a correctable error).

When one of these events occur, the memory subsystem should provide the facilities to:

- Continue servicing memory requests to the failing DIMM
- Copy the current contents of the failing DIMM to the spare
- Update all the system address decoders (located at all the requestors of system).

In the event that the spare DIMM is located behind the same memory controller as the failing DIMM, the copying of the DIMM image is completely hidden from the system interconnect, and as such, falls outside the scope of any algorithms or mechanisms defined by the Intel QuickPath Architecture.

For cases where the failing DIMM is located behind a different memory controller than the spare DIMM, implementations may utilize Intel Quick-Path Interconnect features for the sparing process. The copy engine implementation can take several forms, such as an implementation completely in hardware, or some background process of a processor. Regardless of the actual implementation, the general concepts utilized are as follows:

- Check to ensure the failing DIMM is no larger then the spare DIMM. Note one cannot spare a 2GB DIMM with a single 1GB DIMM.

- Using different message classes (remember coherent transactions use HOM/DRS/NDR) the copy engine will take the image from the failing DIMM over the system topology to the spare. The message classes used for these operations are Non Coherent Standard (NCS) and Non Coherent Bypass (NCB). As can be seen in Figure 5.1, the DIMM copy should not rely on the same message classes (HOM) for the copy in order to avoid any circular dependencies (deadlock).

Note | The primary reason the copy engine should use different message classes is to avoid introducing some type of interdependence resulting in a form of livelock or most likely deadlock. Implementations built to the Intel QPI requirements follow strict dependency rules between the message classes to guarantee deadlock free operation.

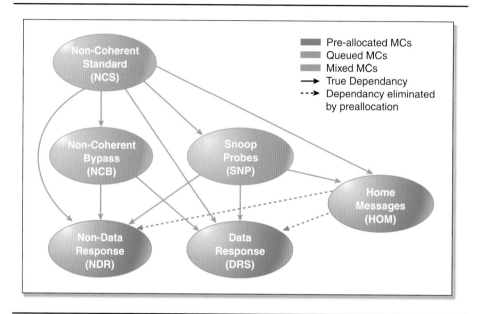

Figure 5.1   Protocol Flow Control Dependencies

■ The NCS message class is used for the data pull operation. (Note: if the copy engine is located on this memory controller the pull is done behind the memory controller and is not observed by the system topology). There are several opcodes (commands) that could be used but the one that would provide the highest bandwidth copy would be Non Coherent Read (NcRd). NcRd will pull a cache line worth of data (64 bytes).

■ The NCB message class is used for the data push operation. (Note: if the copy engine is located on the memory controller of the spare, the push is done behind the memory controller and is not observed by the system topology). There are several opcodes (commands) that could be used but the one that would provide the highest bandwidth copy would be Non Coherent Write (NcWr) or Write Combining Write (WcWr). Either of these two opcodes can push a complete cache line.

■ The simplest method for a copy engine is to have the operating system, prior to the copy, first bring the memory offline and flush all the caches of the system (assuming the particular memory range is in coherent space). After the completion of the copy, update system address decoders to point to the spare DIMM and then signal the OS to bring the particular memory range back online.

This cannot always be done for all memory regions due to "pinned" memory, interrupt tables, OS kernel assumptions, and so on. The most versatile technique is for the copy engine to perform the copy to the spare DIMM while the memory on the failing DIMM still has the potential of being accessed. In the simple case of reads this is not an issue due to the fact that the value of the memory location is unchanged. The end cases that should be managed are the write cases that are exposed to the memory subsystems as implicit or explicit writebacks. A common solution to cover the writeback cases is to spawn an additional write to the spare DIMM (as stated earlier over the NCB message class) in addition to the writing to the failed DIMM. Doing the double write during the time of the memory copy and updating the system address decoders ensures that the system will maintain coherency through this transitional period.

Benefits/Costs of DIMM Sparing

The primary benefit of any feature like this is in the areas of availability and reliability. The primary benefit for the DIMM sparing is that for additional memory availability all that is required is the dedication of a single DIMM. In a 32 DIMM system, 31 can directly be used for system and user applications. One only needs a single spare tire whether a vehicle has 2, 4, 6, or more, tires.

The primary cost of the DIMM sparing feature can be summarized into two major items. The first is the copy engine. It can be very complex. Note that if the user would like to perform the copy and the failed DIMM is mapped to memory space and if that memory range is still in use, then the copy engine should not only deal with the copying of the memory range (in some sequential order) but also handle all implicit and explicit writebacks during the coping to the spare DIMM and up through the transition of the system address decoders to point to the spare DIMM.

The second item is that DIMM sparing feature is predicated on the notion that the failure of the DIMM will not be instantaneous, but instead be a detectable degradation over time. DIMM sparing does not protect the user from a memory access that took an uncorrectable memory read or a DIMM that completely fails prior the completion of the copy.

Memory Mirroring

Memory mirroring is an availability feature that provides a "second copy" of a given memory location. In the event of a failing location the secondary copy of the location provides the data. At any time there exist two locations for every memory location guaranteeing no loss of data. This is a logical next step from the previously discussed DIMM sparing, which dealt with the failure of a single DIMM. Mirroring focuses on surviving through the loss of arbitrary memory addresses all the way through an entire memory controller.

Note | *There are several possible methods of implementing a memory mirrored subsystem and the one provided here is only one example.*

In general terms, as a platform is being configured (let's refer to this as time 0), the distributed memory subsystem maps two memory subsystems to the same address range. The composite memory subsystem from a system perspective is one half the total size of the complete memory subsystem. For a given system address there will be a primary and a mirrored (or secondary) memory subsystem. This is typically implemented with multiple memory controllers in a system, with some configured as primaries and others as secondaries with backup copies of the primaries. Primaries and secondaries will be paired up by BIOS, and Intel QPI requires that the secondary be dedicated to this function and nothing else.

Normal Memory Write or Read Flows (Operation Before a Failure)

Since a memory location is "mirrored" as a memory update occurs, it is the function of the primary memory subsystem to "write" the new value to the mirrored location. The typical operational write flow of the update is as follows, assuming both the primary and mirrored subsystems are operational:

- Originator issues a Write to the primary memory subsystem (using a NonSnpWr/WbMtoI flow) in the HOM message class.

- Primary memory subsystem (for this location) issues a non-coherent write (using an NcWr or NonSnpWr flow) to the mirrored subsystem, containing the data received in the original write. It also posts the write to the primary memory location.

- Mirrored subsystem posts the write to the secondary memory location and then completes the NonSnpWr/NcWr transaction (issues a CMP to the primary memory system).

- Primary memory subsystem completes the write to the original requester (issues a CMP to the originator) once the completion from the secondary has been received.

The typical operational read flow for a mirrored subsystem is exactly the same as normal read flow.

- Originator issues a read to the primary memory subsystem (using a RdCur / RdCode / RdData / RdInvOwn / NonSnpRd opcode) in the HOM message class.

  For a coherent transaction the corresponding snoops are issued, either by the originator (in the source snoop configuration), or the primary memory subsystem (in the home snoop configurations).

  The snoop responses are collected by the primary memory subsystem.

- If an implicit writeback occurs due to snooping (RspIWb snoop response is an example), the primary subsystem will post the data to the local memory as well as triggering the NcWr/NonSnpWr flow to the secondary that was discussed above.

- Data is either provided by the memory subsystem or another caching agent per the Intel QPI protocol.

  If data is to be supplied by the memory subsystem, then the local memory data is used unless it is determined to be corrupted. If the data is not corrupted, then no traffic is sent to the secondary.

- Primary memory subsystem completes the transaction (in the case where data is provided by the memory subsystem the complete can be embedded into the DataC_* message).

Memory Read or Write from Mirrored Image (Living through a Failure)

In the event that the primary memory subsystem has failed, the following are possible write and read flows of a mirrored memory subsystem. These flows are used in transition phase when a given system address has only a single memory location.

The failed operational write flow of the update is as follows:

- Originator issues a write to the primary memory subsystem (using a NonSnpWr/WbMtoI flow) in the HOM message class.

- Primary memory subsystem (for this location) has deemed that this memory location and/or some portion of this memory subsystem has failed. It issues a non-coherent write (using a NonSnpWr/NcWr flow) to the mirrored subsystem.

- Mirrored subsystem posts the write to the secondary memory location and then completes the NonSnpWr/NcWr transaction (issues a CMP to the Primary memory system).

- Primary memory subsystem completes the write to the original requester (issues a CMP to the originator) once the completion from the secondary has been received.

The failed operational read flow for a mirrored subsystem is similar to the normal read flow.

- Originator issues a read to the primary memory subsystem (using a RdCur / RdCode / RdData / RdInvOwn / NonSnpRd opcode) in the HOM message class.

For a coherent transaction then the corresponding snoops are issued, either by the originator (in the source snoop configuration), or the primary memory subsystem (in the home snoop configurations).

The snoop responses are collected by the primary memory subsystem.

■ If an implicit writeback occurs due to snooping (RspIWb snoop response is an example), the primary subsystem will trigger the NcWr/NonSnpWr flow to the secondary that was discussed above, and wait for the completion from the secondary before proceeding.

■ If there was cache to cache transfer of data, such that no data is required from the memory subsystem, then the primary memory subsystem does not need to issue any transactions to the secondary. It can complete the original transaction immediately.

■ If data is required from memory, the primary issues a non-coherent read (using a NonSnpRd/NcRd flow) to the mirrored subsystem. Information is encoded into this transaction to indicate the ID of the originator and the final cache state to be sent. This encoding is product-specific. At this point, the primary is done with the transaction.

■ Mirrored subsystem services the NonSnpRd/NcRd and creates the appropriate DataC_<I/E/S/F>_Cmp/FrcAckCnflt message. This includes the original transaction's ID information sent in the non-coherent read, along with the data from the secondary's mirrored copy of memory. This packet is then sent to the originator.

Again these are the flows intended to be used until either the primary subsystem can be brought offline and all transactions can be directed to the mirror subsystem or a new primary subsystem can be brought online. The additional transactions between the primary and the secondary make them undesirable from a performance point of view for sustained use.

Memory Mirroring Re-Silvering Process

During the time when one of the primary memory images has failed in a system, the system is relying on a single image at the secondary and cannot tolerate an additional unrecoverable memory error from there. The fundamental steps taken by the system management system to "re-silver" the memory mirror are as follows:

■ Quiesce the system.

■ Take the mirror out of secondary mode and place it in primary mode. Also take the primary out of primary mirroring mode.

■ Remap the system to send requests for the memory region to the ID of what used to be the secondary. This entity will now be the primary for accesses to this memory.

■ Dequiesce the system.

At this point, the system is running, but still not re-enabled with mirrored memory for the new primary. To reconstruct mirroring operations, the following should be done.

■ Initialize a new memory subsystem to be used as the secondary. This can either be a new memory entity, or the old primary with a repaired memory channel. Program this new entity in secondary mirroring mode.

■ Pair the primary with the newly available secondary. This flow is product-specific, but may require a Quiesce.

■ From the active memory subsystem "push" an image of the entire primary memory.

■ During "push" continue to issue mirrored writes (just as if when performing a normal memory mirror operation).

During the time of the memory copy (the push) there can exist a race condition where an "operational write" is initiated by a requester as older data is being copied in the re-silvering process. To avoid any issues the new write should be stalled until the write of the older data is completed.

Benefits/Costs of Memory Mirroring

The primary benefit of any feature like this is in the area of availability and reliability. Memory mirroring gives a system the ability to survive what would otherwise have been unrecoverable memory errors.

The cost of memory mirroring:

- Copy engine can be very complex. It should handle the ability of the bulk copy as well as the incremental writes and should handle the address conflict between the bulk copy with an operational write.

- Requires twice the number of DIMMs for the memory subsystem.

- Consumes system bandwidth to keep the primary and mirror images in sync.

- Writes to the secondary cannot share virtual network VN0 or VN1 with any non-preallocated traffic in the same virtual channels on a link, to prevent potential deadlock.

- DRS-based mirroring traffic cannot share a virtual network with non-mirroring DRS traffic.

Memory Migration

Memory migration is a feature that has several usage models, a few of these are

- Replacing a failing memory subsystem without bringing down a system. This assumes that the failing subsystem can be detected before any uncorrectable data loss occurs.

- Bring a memory subsystem offline for a memory upgrade.

- Allow for dynamic repartitioning of a system without loss of memory contents in the "running" portion of the partition.

Memory migration uses similar copy engines to DIMM sparing and the memory mirroring re-silvering process (or a system configuration agent could use the Quiesce/Dequiesce feature of Intel QPI to allow a core to perform the copy as well). If a component implements memory mirroring, the memory migration flow can utilize a subset of these features to implement memory migration. The destination of the migration can be considered a mirroring secondary. Once the source memory and the destination memory are paired together, data can be migrated using the Write Mirroring flows discussed in the previous section. Once all memory addresses in the region have been "pushed" to the secondary, it can be unpaired with the primary and become the new primary owner of the memory.

Power Management

The Intel QuickPath Architecture has provided methods to manage the power of an individual link (link power management), as well as defining a protocol layer power management message. This second messaging construct provides the agents of a system with the ability to negotiate different system or component states (S-State, C-State, and P-State changes).

Link Power Management

The link power management control (excluding the overall enables) is completely controlled by the Intel QPI link layer. This differs from the PCIe model of similar link power management features where their definition and control spans more then one architectural layer. Intel QuickPath Interconnect link power management features are:

- L0s – L0 Sleep state. L0s has independent control. Each transmitter controls the entry/exit of the L0s state. This means that for a given endpoint, the receiver side of the link-pair could be in an L0s state and its transmitter in the L0 state, or vice versa.

- L1 - L1 offers a lower power state than L0s, but requires additional latency to wake to L0. In L1, one key difference is that the forwarded clocks are disabled, whereas in L0s they remain enabled. In addition, L1 affects the state of the entire link-pair (not a unidirectional state like L0s or L0p)

- L0p – L0p Partial width state is the capability of an Intel QPI link (per direction) that allow reducing the link width from 20 lanes to 10 (or 10 lanes to 5), and the reverse. As with L0s, L0p is managed on a per direction basis.

The support for L0s, L0p and L1 are product optional features.

L0s Link State

To provide flexibility to dynamically adapt to different workloads that can be experienced during normal runtime, the optional L0s mechanism is available as an aid in limiting Intel QPI link power consumption. L0s enables the link to reduce power consumption during periods when a transmitter has nothing to send and relatively low wakeup latency is needed to bring the link back into a normal operating L0 state. The Intel QPI link allows for the configuration of L0s exit times.

The intention of this configurable mechanism is to allow a link to manage power itself to the greatest extent possible while still meeting the latency goals of the system at any given time. Once a given latency tolerance is determined by a mechanism such as the system power state and other operating conditions, a wake time can be assigned to the link indicating how much time is allowed for waking from the L0s state. Once this is configured, a port can power down all circuits on the transmitters and receivers that are not needed to guarantee recovery to L0 in the required amount of time once a break event occurs. In particular, the forwarded clock is not powered down during L0s, it continues to run between the two devices. This allows a relatively fast-waking L0s state that achieves minimal power savings when latency is critical, or a slower-waking L1 state that achieve greater power reductions to be used when power requirements dominate.

L0s Link Entry Entry into the L0s state is managed separately for each direction of the link-pair. It is the responsibility of each transmitter to initiate an entry into the L0s state on its transmitting lanes when needed.

There is no specified policy for invoking the L0s state. It is left to the implementation to determine the appropriate amount of idle time to wait before deciding to enter into the L0s state after the last non-Idle packet has been sent. Once a decision to enter L0s has been made, a transmitter sends the PM.LinkEnterL0s flit. Following this, the transmitter disables most of it's transmit lanes and transitions from the L0 state to the L0s state.

L0s Link State While a transmitter/receiver is in L0s state, 19 of the 20 lanes are disabled. The only two lanes being driven by the transmitter are a single lane called the sense lane in addition to the forwarded clock.

L0s Link Exit The transmitters in the L0s state initiate an exit to L0 before being able to send packets across the link. Exiting of L0s state to L0 is initiated by the Tx side of the link. The reasons for the transmitter to exit the L0s state are

- ■ To return link layer credits to avoid possible deadlock scenarios.
- ■ To send protocol layer packets required by the agent.
- ■ To perform physical layer retraining in this link direction.

The Tx signals the start of the L0s exit by transitioning the sense lane. During L0s, this sense lane has been held in a static differential state. When the sense lane transitions, the wake up process of the other 19 lanes at the Tx and Rx happens, and this link direction transitions to the operational link state L0.

L0p Link State

The Intel QuickPath Architecture, in addition to supporting L0s, has provided a feature to manage the width of a given direction. This feature allows the endpoints to determine if a link should be (at a given moment) 20, 10, or 5 lanes wide. In L0p, the width is managed separately for each direction of the link-pair (exactly as L0s is managed). It is the responsibility of each transmitter to determine the appropriate directional width.

There is no specified policy for invoking the L0p state. It is left to the implementation to determine the appropriate amount of idle time and link bandwidth consumed, to determine when to change the link width in each direction. The transmitter uses PM.LinkWidthConfig to indicate the new link width.

L0p Link Decision Unlike L0s, there is no "real" L0p link state, this is just a mechanism to shift the link width up (or down). The decision process is based on what flit rate is needed for the given direction. Every time a link "downshifts," the flit rate is reduced by one half and the time to deliver a flit on the wire doubles. The benefit of an "upshift" is that for every upshift the available flit rate doubles; the negative impact is the increased power consumption. Table 5.1 shows the latency impact for a single flit for the different link widths.

Table 5.1 Flit Time versus Link Width

Link Width	Flit Transfer Time	Request Time	Cache Line Transfer Time (64 Bytes / 9 Flits)	Powered lanes including clocks – per direction
20 Lanes	2 Clocks	2 Clocks	18 Clocks	21 Lanes
10 Lanes	4 Clocks	4 Clocks	36 Clocks	11 Lanes
5 Lanes	8 Clocks	8 Clocks	72 Clocks	6 Lanes

L1 Link State

L1 support is optional. Usage of this state will be determined and optionally enabled following link initialization by the algorithms that use the Intel QPI power management infrastructure. It is expected that the platform power supplies remain on during the L1 state. L1 offers a lower power state than L0s, but can cause additional latency to wake to L0. In L1, one key difference is that the forwarded clocks are disabled, whereas in L0s they remain active. As with the forwarded clocks being disabled in the L1 state, the PLLs controlling these clocks could also be disabled.

Unlike L0s, which allows independence for the two directions of the link-pair, L1 requires the lanes in both directions to enter the L1 state. This makes the entering of L1 state from L0 to be a negotiated transition between the two link endpoints. To simplify entry into L1 state, a master-slave concept is used to negotiate the link level entry to L1. Each link-pair has one endpoint dedicated to be the master with the other being the slave. The initiation of an L1 entry negotiation through a PM.LinkEnterL1 link layer message is done by the master while the slave has the task to acknowledge or not acknowledge this incoming request. The master/slave setting are done during system initialization (usually determined by some firmware algorithm or system service processor) while the link is in slow-speed mode of operation. It should be noted that all link low power states are not allowed during slow mode operation. The settings then take effect after the link transitions to at-speed operation.

As with the other Link Power States (L0s and L0p) the determination of when to initiate transitions to the link L1 state is left up to the platform vendor. Once these conditions are met, the master of the link issues a PM.LinkEnterL1 message to the slave. Upon reception the link message, the slave of the link replies with either a PM.LinkReqAck or a PM.LinkReqNack or a Link Level Retry.

Note

It stands to reason that the same rules the master uses to initiate an L1 transition, such as no outstanding traffic, no significant number of credits to return, and so on, will apply to the slave to either acknowledge or not acknowledge the request to go to the L1 state.

L1 Link Entry As stated earlier, it is the platform or system architecture that provides the algorithm for a link-pair to enter L1. One could expect several criteria to be met prior to the L1 request:

- No outstanding protocol request has been issued down this link. The requests would appear in the HOM, NCS, or NCB message classes.

- There is no currently posted snoop requiring a snoop response to be sent down this link.

- There is no currently outstanding request that requires a snoop to be sent down this link.

- The link layer does not have a large number of VNA, VN0, or VN1 credits to be returned.

- The link layer does not have a large number of Acks (for the Link Layer Retry buffer to be returned.

When the link L1 entry conditions are met, the master is allowed to issue a PM.LinkEnterL1. The master stops issuing any protocol packets until either a PM.LinkReqNack is received or the link is brought down into L1. In short, the Enter_L1 and L1_Ack messages (PM.LinkEnterL1 and PM.LinkReqAck) may not be interleaved in any protocol layer packet. The message is injected on an idle link. The reasons for this are to prevent the unwanted delay in transmission of the protocol packet, avoid the unnecessary power cycling of a link, and to avoid the unnecessary latency addition for this transaction.

In the case the slave responds with a PM.LinkReqNack, the backpressure applied by the master to the protocol layers can be removed and transactions are allowed to flow over the link. Also, the master can only issue a single PM.LinkReqAck and the slave responds with either a PM.LinkReqNack or PM.LinkReqAck.

Note	*What has been described in this subsection is the typical negotiation of a link-pair attempting to enter L1. Another possible exiting of this negotiation is due to a CRC error and a link layer retry request.*

L1 Link State After the master has received the PM.LinkReqAck, it initiates the link going down.

If the slave chooses to ACK this request, it alerts its physical layer indicating that the next received inband reset will be an indication to go to link L1 state. And once this ACK is received and decoded by the link layer of the master agent, it will alert its own physical layer to go to the L1 state by asserting an inband reset to the remote (slave) agent. Once the inband reset is asserted by the master, the master transitions into L1 state without waiting for the incoming inband reset from the slave side. Once the inband reset initiated by the master is received by the slave agent, the slave moves to the L1 state as well and returns the inband reset to the master.

Once PM.LinkReqAck is received by the master, the master will ignore any subsequent flits, and will not decode them until the links get through L1 and get back out to L0. Once the master initiates the L1 entry to the slave through an inband reset event, it continues to drive a DC value on the clock lane for a short period. During this time, it may also start turning its drivers and receivers off. Any agent that enters L1 state sets all the Rx (both CLK and DATA) terminations to HIGH while turning on its link detect circuitry (with the associated impedance) for its CLK and DATA transmitters.

L1 Link Exit Exit from L1 is independent of the master/slave designation, and can be initiated by either endpoint. Fundamentally, the exiting of L1 (from a link perspective) looks like the physical layer detection and initialization sequence. One difference is that the link remembers the clock rate and powers on and initializes "at speed." There is no slow mode to "at speed" transition as in a power on sequence.

The endpoint that is gearing up to signal an exit condition needs to first ramp its clock up and get to a state where it can attain proper functionality. At that point in time, it makes the transition from L1 to the Detect.ClkTerm state in its physical layer. This transition sets the Rx clock termination to ground for this particular agent, which is then picked up as an analog wake-up signal by the remote agent. The rest of the sequence is exactly like a link initialization sequence (from a physical layer perspective).

Platform Power Management

The Intel QuickPath Architecture defines a protocol layer packet to carry system and component layer power management requests. Platform power management requests are used to manage a set of power states, usually managed by software (the OS), which governs the power policy and usage for a platform or a partition within that platform. For the platform there are 4 major power state sets, which are designated S, C, P, and T. For all the states discussed, the lower the number of that state, the higher the power, so S0, C0, T0, and P0 would have the highest power consumption and performance for their state type. When relative levels of power states are being referred to, it is natural to refer to lower numbered states as "higher states" or "higher power states," and so on.

- *C-states* govern the power management state of the platform processor(s) as defined in the ACPI specification. The different states define various functional levels of service the processor can provide to the system.

- *P-states* govern the relative power versus performance point at which a platform is operating so as to allow a platform to make informed decisions about power versus performance tradeoffs. P-states are expected to represent better than linear power savings for the performance impact (that is, a 50 percent performance degradation should result in more than 50 percent power savings).

- *T-states,* or Throttling states, are similar to P-states in that they represent a measure of power versus performance tradeoff. They differ from P-states since they are expected to result in a linear power reduction for the resulting performance degradation (that is, a 50 percent performance degradation would result in a 50 percent power decrease).

- *S-States* govern the system power state as defined in the ACPI specification. These states are typically different types of system suspend states.

People differentiate between two primary categories of power states. The first category is composed of C, P, and T-states and involves different components or threads on the platform that can be at different levels of these states at the same time.

The second category is composed of S-states and involves an entire system entering into a suspend state in an orderly manner. The mechanisms for the two categories are very similar, but there are some subtle differences that justify treating them separately.

The Intel QuickPath Architecture does not address which type of the power states are used or the policy for determining when there should be a "state" change but it does define how the state change is negotiated.

The negotiation policy is an "ask" policy, in short, "Can I go to this new lower power state?" The requester "asks" all Node IDs in its set. The set of Node IDs provide a response with the maximum allowed state the Node ID is allowed to enter. Note the set of Node IDs could be all the Node IDs of a platform, or of a partition, or a combined list of Node IDs of multiple partitions (in the case where there is some shared resource between partitions).

An example of the "ask" negotiation policy is provided in Figure 5.2. In this example the "requester" is attempting to lower its P-state from P1 to P4 (P4 being a lower P-state) and the set of Node IDs are {A, B, C} where B is "asking" for a P-state change.

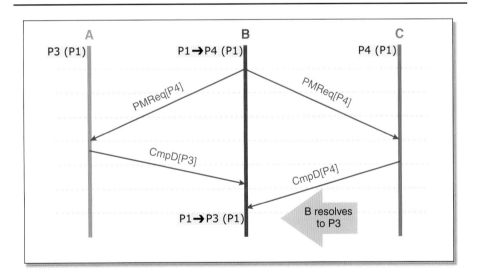

Figure 5.2 Power Management Negotiation Example

The final P-state of B in this example is a transition from P1 to P3; note it was the response from A that prevented B from going all to P4.

PM Messages

The negotiation policy is basically a multicast of the power state request change and the set of responses from the set of Node IDs. Intel QPI has a protocol layer message defined specifically for this "ask" negotiation, the PM-Req message. Each node receiving the PMReq message is required to provide a completion response that indicates the lowest power state that it can tolerate the requester entering. The PMReq protocol message uses the NcMsg format. The completion response used is the CmpD message.

Fault Detection and Reporting

The level of fault detection usually varies between market segment (mission-critical platforms clearly have more stringent fault detection and reporting capability than the high end desktop platforms). As a general guide line it is the expectations of the platform segment that dictate the level of fault detection. The Intel QuickPath Architecture provides multiple methods to report and diagnose the platform.

Error Reporting Methods

The Intel QuickPath Architecture supports the following reporting methods:

- Error reporting via an interrupt message. In particular, the IntPhysical or IntLogical packet with SMI/Machine Check Abort delivery mode can be used to trigger the appropriate interruption for an error event.

- A failed completion of an Intel QPI transaction can be indicated by asserting RspStatus = Failed in a response packet. Upon receiving this response packet, the original requester should take a Machine Check Abort.

- A corrupt data flit can be indicated by asserting the Poison bit in a data flit. See Chapter 6 for more details on data poisoning.

- A corrupt header flit can be indicated by asserting the Viral bit in a header flit. See Chapter 6 for more details on the Viral indication.

- A corrected platform event (CPE) can be reported to the legacy IO agent by issuing a NcMsgB with a CPE sub-opcode indication.

Fault Diagnosis

In general, for fault diagnosis, information is logged in hardware registers associated with the type of error that has occurred. This information is then accessed either using Intel QPI transactions through the system fabric, or using out-of-band methods such as SMBus. For systems based on Intel QPI technology, many types of errors that can occur will be the same regardless of platform and market segment. Many other error types, however, will depend on the component architecture as dictated by market segment needs, size of the system, implementation of optional Intel QPI features, and more. The Intel QuickPath Architecture has defined logging registers and fields for the common error types, mostly centered on link-related errors in the physical layer and the link layer. While error indications, such as Poison and Viral (discussed further in Chapter 6), are defined by the architecture, no specific logging registers are required for them. Components may decide to provide additional error indication capabilities going beyond those required by the architecture.

Physical Layer

The physical layer has the largest set of defined hardware registers of any layer. Along these same lines, it also has the largest set of architecturally defined error registers and fault information. The ability to diagnose errors at this layer is critical for numerous reasons.

First, the physical layer is the point of connection between two Intel QPI components. As such, any fault that occurs in this level is likely to have upstream effects on the upper layers attempting to use the link. These effects could be visible to one or both of the components. To ensure that the appropriate data is available for interpreting a failure, a common implementation of logging information is critical.

This is also the layer where, due to the high speed signaling nature of Intel QPI, faults can be extremely hard to isolate or repeat. The physical layer is an "always on" connection, in that there is no concept of a stall or stopping of transmitted information. This means that even if no protocol layer traffic is occurring, data is still being transmitted (typically in the form of NULL flits) which can source faults. The result may be errors that are not associated with any running process or code in the system, meaning only hardware-based logging can provide the necessary information.

Lastly, many of the functions of the physical layer include the ability to heal around faults (see Chapter 6 for more discussion). In these cases, a link may continue to operate in the presence of errors, but not at its maximal capability. In these instances, it is necessary for information to be available to system software to indicate the reasons that these types of healing features have been engaged.

Link Layer

The link layer has a smaller set of architecturally defined registers, but it again focuses on defining the information that would be common across Intel QPI components. The link layer defines errors related to the Parameter Exchange state machine, as well as CRC and the Link Level Retry state machine. Status information related to these is listed in a Link Status register, although the definition is not exhaustive or representative of the full amount of information that a component could provide. These fields provide a common starting point of critical information. Because errors can be transitive in nature, as discussed with the physical layer, it is helpful for components to log information related to their implementation of these mechanisms.

Protocol Layer

The protocol layer has no architecturally defined set of hardware registers. There is no defined set of fault logging information for timeout errors or error indications such as Failed Responses, Viral, or Poison (see Chapter 6 for definitions of these). This does not mean that information should not be logged for these occurrences; it is merely an indication of how varied the hardware implementations of various pieces of the protocol layer may be from block to block within a chip, and between various chips.

It is helpful with protocol layer failures to give pointers to where the error occurred, as these failures are likely tied to code that is executing in the system.

As an example, for Transaction Timeouts, typical information that may be logged include the type of transaction that timed out, the system address the transaction was targeting (if defined), and the Node ID the transaction was targeting. This information alone is highly variable in size given the various scalability options of Intel QPI, which is one reason for the lack of specific register definitions.

Interrupts

Intel QPI supports two APIC interrupt architecture definitions, these being XAPIC for IA-32 and SAPIC for the Intel® Itanium® processor family, by providing interrupt packets that appear in the NCB message class. These packets provide the basic mechanisms for processors to send interrupts to other processors (IPIs); I/O XAPIC to send interrupts to processors; as well as I/O devices directly generating interrupt messages through PCI/PCIe message signaled interrupt (MSI) or equivalent mechanism.

The Intel QuickPath Architecture also carries forward the constructs of interrupts, interrupt acknowledgment, and end of interrupt (EOI) of legacy 8259A modes; however, this interrupt architecture also assumes that there is only one active 8259A equivalent interrupt controller in a given partition.

The complete list of interrupt messages provided in Intel QPI is contained in Table 5.2.

Table 5.2   Intel® QPI Mapping of System Interrupt Messages

Interrupt Message	Description
IntPhysical	Physical Mode Interrupt Message destined to a core (s)
IntLogical	Logical Mode Interrupt Message destined to a core (s)
EOI	Legacy 8259A End of Interrupt Message
INTR	Legacy 8259A Interrupt Signal
SMI	Interrupt to a core signaling it to enter System Management Mode (SMM)
NMI	Interrupt to a core that a Non-Maskable Interrupt has occurred
IntAck	In Legacy 8259A mode this transaction (which is similar to read request) returns the vector of the interrupt that is to be serviced.

In short, Intel QPI provides the complete mapping of all interrupt modes for the IA-32 and Intel® Itanium® Processor Family system architectures. The encodings provided are versatile enough to support XAPIC (including the new extended mode), the old legacy 8259A modes (still used in the boot process in some systems), as well as the Intel® Itanium® SAPIC modes.

It should be noted that

- Intel QuickPath Architecture does not define how the APIC IDs are assigned nor the relationship of the APIC ID to an agent's Node ID.

- Target processor contexts should be specified with each interrupt message. In addition, distinction are made between interrupt message for Physical mode and Logical mode interrupts, and this distinction is used by the processors to match specified targets with either the Physical APIC ID or the Logical APIC ID, to register an interrupt with the correct processor context.

- All APICs are either configured in the Legacy or Extended modes.

- For each interrupt event, only one interrupt message is sent to each Intel QPI processor entity, which is then responsible for transmitting the interrupt message to one or all local processor contexts. There is no restriction on the number of interrupt messages being sent to a processor entity for different interrupt events at any time; that is, multiple interrupt requests from a source to the same or different processors may be pipelined.

In addition Intel QPI also supports the APIC ability for directed and redirectable interrupts. In the case of redirectable interrupts an interrupt from an agent is sent to the core that is running at the lowest priority. This information of the priority of a core is conveyed to the I/O subsystem via the Intel QPI Interrupt Priority Update command (IntPrioUpd).

Delivery Methods

Typically interrupts from I/O devices or inter-processor interrupts (IPIs) are delivered on Intel QPI using the IntPhysical or IntLogical request with an address in the interrupt delivery region of the system address map. Part of the address field contains the Local APIC ID of the target processor context for the interrupt. The interrupt delivery mechanism supports the lowest priority interrupt delivery mode. The lowest priority delivery mode may be used only with I/O initiated interrupt messages.

As stated earlier, Intel QPI supports the concept of redirection of low priority interrupts. The purpose of redirection is to enable lowest priority interrupt delivery to improve performance through interrupt distribution, taking into account task priority levels among processor contexts and other factors (like power state and frequency of a given processor). In addition to the IntPhysical and IntLogical messages, redirection utilizes the IntPrioUpd transaction to facilitate interrupt redirection. The IntPrioUpd transaction provides indications regarding the task priority level at the processor context, decode type to determine logical addressing mode, and if the Local APIC is disabled. This transaction is sent from processor entities to all the I/O proxy entities that may receive a redirectable interrupt from I/O devices. This transaction may be sent to entities other than I/O proxy entities; however, other entities may ignore the contents of this transaction and reply with a Cmp response.

The exact redirection algorithm used in a system is implementation-dependent. Care is taken such that the interrupt is registered at exactly one of the Local APICs by selecting among the APICs indicated in the interrupt request and avoiding any APICs that are disabled. Some of the ways of optimizing interrupt performance such as balanced distribution of interrupts among all processor contexts and localization of interrupts with specific vectors to specific processor contexts to avoid cache thrashing may play a role in selection of a target for redirectable interrupts. Again, Intel QPI provides the mechanisms to implement redirection but the best algorithm for redirection is platform-specific.

Example Interrupt Flows

As stated earlier, Intel QPI has defined the mechanisms to support the 8259 legacy transactions; however, the typical case is the support for the APIC messages (that is SAPIC, XAPIC, and extended XAPIC). In the typical case the protocol agent initiating the interrupt may decode the address field to determine the target Intel QPI Node ID (the agent has a mapping of APIC ID to Node ID) and sends either IntPhysical or IntLogical request to the target entity or to all the processor entities. In the case of a redirectable interrupt the protocol agent (via predetermined algorithm) selects the correct APIC ID to issue the interrupt(s).

The IntPhysical and IntLogical interrupt requests appear in the non-coherent bypass (NCB) message class. The interrupt message being one of the more infrequently occurring transactions was mapped to the largest NCB packet size (eleven flits). The data payload of the message contains specifics of the APIC message such as the interrupt vector, the delivery and trigger modes.

System Management

A system based on Intel QuickPath Interconnect links could always use out-of-band methods to manage the system resources. A few of these out-of-band interfaces that have been used in the past are SMBus, PECI, and JTAG. Such interfaces provide access to configuration registers, performance counters, system audit trails, error logs, and so on. It should be noted that Intel QPI architecture does not preclude the use of any out-of-band interface nor does it require these types of interfaces. In addition Intel QPI does not preclude the use of both in-band and out-of-band methods at the same time. This is clearly left as a decision of the system implementer.

As stated earlier in this book, Intel QPI defines a list of agent types that are involve in various transactions. In addition to the two most common agents (home and caching), there is also the concept of a *configuration agent*. The purpose of the configuration agent is to allow a system service processor to issue configuration accesses to the control registers of a given socket.

Configuration Space Access

The system configuration register set includes the address decode registers and switch route tables but may not include processor core model-specific registers (MSRs) or any other processor configuration registers internal to the core and not accessible via loads/stores.

In systems that support multiple partitions, the system configuration registers are classified into two sets: protected and unprotected. The protected set includes all configuration registers that can affect the operation of multiple partitions. Registers belonging to this set should not be accessible by an OS but rather controlled by out-of-band and in-band system management entities. The address decode registers and the route tables are examples of registers that belong in this set. The unprotected set may include error logging and performance monitoring registers that should be accessible by software (that is, by the OS of a partition). The exact membership list in each set is platform architecture and usage model dependent. For example, the protected set is likely to be an empty set in a platform that does not support multiple partitions.

In the event that a register access is allowed over the Intel QPI–based system topology, Intel QPI has defined four configuration commands:

- Configuration Read – NcCfgRd in the NCS Message class
- Configuration Write – NcCfgWr in the NCS Message Class
- Non-Coherent Read – NcRd in the NCS Message class
- Non-Coherent Write – NcWr in the NCB Message class

Note

> One should not confuse the Configuration commands with the non-coherent commands (NcRd / NcRdPtl / NcWr / NcWrPtl). The configuration commands target the address space usually accessed by a core issuing a xCF8/xCFC access. The NcRd / NcWr(Ptl) are used for configuration registers that are directly mapped into the system memory address space.

Summary

This chapter has described in general terms how several complex system functions employed in larger systems can be accomplished in a platform based on the Intel QuickPath Interconnect. In the next chapter we explore how the Intel QuickPath Interconnect not only provides a high performance interface for enabling these sort of system functions, but it also has provisions to detect and tolerate errors, making for a more reliable and robust interconnect.

Chapter 6

RAS and DFx Features

Watson's Law: The reliability of machinery is inversely proportional to the number and significance of any persons watching it.

—Unknown

In this chapter we deal with the concerns of reliability, availability, and serviceability, which are collectively labeled RAS features. One subset of those features consists of those capabilities typically used for out of service Test, Debug, or Validation functions. A common nomenclature for the many "Design For (fill in the blank)" is DFx.

Reliability features in general exist in order to provide the system a robust method of delivering the required performance and data integrity levels despite the occurrence of certain events. Error correction logic on memory interfaces is a typical example. Availability features have to do with allowing the system to continue to perform useful work even in the presence of some event that may have degraded performance. An example here could include the loss of a portion of a physical interconnect. DFx features can include self-test capabilities, or the ability to capture and analyze information from the system under test. Later in this chapter we provide a brief overview of possible probing techniques for capturing information from an Intel® Quick-Path Interconnect (Intel QPI) link. We will show that the infrastructure provided goes beyond a single link.

Bit Error Detection and Recovery

As discussed earlier in Chapter 3, the Intel QPI link has been architected from inception to survive bit flips (or transmission errors) and still provide a reliable delivery medium. A key component of the link layer reliability strategy is based on having the transmitter append to every flit (72-bit payload) eight bits of CRC resulting in the total flit size of 80 bits. The receiving link layer checks the CRC of each incoming flit. Upon detection of an error, the receiver throws away the flit in error, and all subsequent flits, and signals to the opposite end that an error has been detected. This forces the transmitter to retry the transmission of the last *n* flits.

CRC Mechanisms

Many contemporary link definitions such as PCI Express™ (PCIe™) expect bit errors on the link and therefore use some validation mechanism as a means to detect errors. Probably the most common checking algorithm for a link is to append a CRC polynominal to all transimissions. In most cases the CRC is over the entire packet. The primary difference for Intel QPI is the CRC code is not over the entire packet and therefore can be a much smaller code word (8 bits versus a 16- or 32-bit CRC polynomial).

Intel QPI has chosen to guarantee delivery not at the granularity of a packet, but instead at that of a flit. This provides two major benefits:

1. Simpler CRC code. Simpler code means that fewer gates are required to implement the polynomial, hence less power and area are consumed and the process is faster.

2. Performance. In the case of CRC across an entire packet, the entire packet is received prior to the data being forwarded (or consumed). An Intel QPI agent is allowed to consume (or forward) a single flit if it has a valid CRC.

The comparison of CRC over a small data quantum (a flit) to a larger one (an entire packet) is very interesting. For adequate protection of a cache line transfer of information (64 bytes of data + header) one would need at least a 32-bit polynomial (similar to PCIe). Also you would have to receive the entire packet and check it prior to forwarding the data on to the requestor (or at every intermediate link hop in a system that is not fully interconnected). The latency impact of this (assuming a 6.4GT/s link transfer rate and 2 bytes per transfer) to the first 8 bytes of data is the additional time waiting for the reception of the next 56 bytes of data, or 4.375 nanoseconds/hop.

Enhanced Protection - Rolling CRC Mechanism

The Rolling CRC algorithm, as discussed in Chapter 3, strikes a balance between increased protection and the performance overhead of a larger polynomial. Moving to a larger polynomial would require either a larger payload in the flits, or moving to a methodology spanning larger quantities of data. Rolling CRC provides better error detection than CRC8 and doesn't change the fundamental CRC encoding in the flits. Rolling CRC does come at the cost of a slight increase in latency. Due to the calculation spanning two flits, an additional flit delay is incurred prior to forwarding (or consuming) a flit. However, rolling CRC still enjoys superior performance characteristics over a CRC covering an entire packet because the delay is fixed at a maximum of one additional flit delay.

The performance of CRC8 versus rolling CRC versus CRC over an entire packet is as follows (assuming 6.4 GT/s):

- CRC8 – Consume the protocol flit immediately (either process the flit or forward it).

- Rolling CRC – Consume the protocol flit 0.625ns later in time (a single flit delay)

- CRC over an entire Packet

- Small Packet (requests, snoops, snoop responses, dataless completions) – Growth of 8 bits to support a 16-bit CRC. Adding 2 extra lanes or increasing the minimum packet size from 80 to 100 bits. The first solution cost is increasing the link width by 10 percent versus the second where the performance impact (and bandwidth loss) is of a 100-bit small packet.

- Large Packet – 4.375ns additional latency to consuming the first 8 bytes of data or to forward the packet to requester (or per hop in the route through case).

Recovery Through Link Layer Retry

The CRC algorithms described previously do an excellent job of detecting and signaling that an error has occurred. These CRC algorithms do not, however, correct the error itself. The Intel QuickPath Architecture, like PCIe, places the burden of the link recovery in the link layer and employs a link layer retry mechanism as the means to survive these routine random transmission errors. This process was described in detail in Chapter 3.

The flows described previously represented a "typical" Intel QPI link level retry, but they by no means described all the possible actions that may occur as more difficult error scenarios are encountered. A few to consider are

- What happens in the case where both sides detect a CRC event in close proximity in time to each other?

- What happens if an LLR.Ack isn't received after a period of time?

- What takes precedence, a link retrain event or a link level retry event?

- What happens in the case of multiple failed retry attempts?

Component designers take into account those and other possible error scenarios and the end result is the total set of features implemented by the devices.

An Intel QPI feature that addresses the last question is of particular interest in the discussion of Intel QPI RAS. The link level retry state machine contains a timeout mechanism that is triggered in the event that an LLR.Req is not responded to with an LLR.Ack after a defined amount of time, or if the retransmitted flit following the LLR.Ack was received with an error. This type of failure could occur due to a one time bit flip on the receiver side of the link. At the expiration of the timeout, the LLR.Req is reattempted, and a one time bit flip on the previous retry attempt would be overcome by retransmitting.

In the case where the error is more serious, preventing numerous LLR.Req attempts from succeeding, something in the interconnection between the two components is more fundamentally wrong. The simple case may be a misalignment between the clock and the data at the receiver, which would be corrected by a retraining of the physical layer to cause clock interpolators to be realigned. For this reason, the link level retry state machine implements a threshold for the maximum number of consecutive failed retry attempts. When this threshold is reached, the link layer resets the physical layer, which in turn stops link layer traffic until L0 is reached, at which time the link level retry can be reattempted. With the misalignment fixed, the retry can succeed and the link proceeds with normal operation. This entire sequence is done without software intervention and without the loss of a single flit.

Beyond the clock and data misalignment problem discussed above, more severe failures may also cause the link layer to reset the physical layer. The following section describes some of the additional failure situations that the physical layer can tolerate and "self-heal" with a reset.

Hard Failure–Tolerant Links

The Intel QuickPath Architecture provides the ability to survive a failed forwarded clock lane and potentially multiple failed data lanes. This might have been accomplished by providing additional spare clock and data lanes, but Intel QPI architects instead chose not to burden the interface with two additional lanes per direction. Remember each lane is differential (two pins) and there are ratios of ground to signal pins that should be maintained. The Intel QPI solutions for continuing to operate in the presence of a failed physical interconnect are

- Data lane failover by utilizing the ability of Intel QPI to support different link widths.
- Clock lane failover by reuse of a data lane to be an alternate clock lane.

The implementation of each of these features is a product optional choice typically provided for the high end market segments. The possible use of connectors in the Intel QPI physical pathways in larger system configurations makes these features useful methods of working around possible failures in the connection. While not precluded, these features would probably not appear where components are usually all interconnected on one PCB with no connectors in the path.

Data Lane Failover

Data lane failover is the ability for an Intel QPI link to tolerate and map out one, or potentially more than one, bad data lane. Data lane failover uses the link's architectural ability to determine and negotiate its final physical width before beginning data transmission. This feature is often referred to as "link self-healing". Link self-healing is generally a feature for platforms in the high availability market segments, where maintaining seamless operation of the system is more critical than total available link bandwidth.

This feature is completely implemented in the physical layer, outside the intervention of other high level layers. During the various states of the physical layer training state machine, individual data lanes can be marked with a LaneDropped attribute if they have failed to meet the exit criteria for a particular state. When the state machine ultimately reaches the state where Link Width is negotiated, an attempt is made to find the maximum width link that can be built with data quadrants that don't have any lanes marked with the Dropped attribute. Note that any single lane in a quadrant being marked LaneDropped will preclude the use of that entire quadrant of 5 lanes. Intel QPI supports link widths of Full (20 bits), Half (10 bits), and Quarter (5 bits). Both ends of the link exchange information on what combinations of quadrants each can support, and a determination is made as to the quadrant(s) that will be made active for data transmission. Table 6.1 provides a rough mapping of the number of detected lanes to the final link width.

Table 6.1 Link Width versus Detect Lanes

Detected Lanes	Link Direction Width
20 Lanes	Full Width (20 lanes)
19–10 Lanes	Half Width (10 lanes)
9–5 Lanes	Quarter Width (5 lanes)

Because data lanes are mapped in quadrants, the number of failed lanes that can be tolerated is dependent on their placement within each quadrant. All five lanes in a quadrant are considered unavailable when negotiating link width even if only one of them has been marked as LaneDropped. As such, it is possible for a working link to be formed even if up to 15 failed lanes were detected, if those 15 failed lanes happen to fall within three quadrants.

Conversely, if the failed data lanes fall into mutually exclusive quadrants, then the maximum number of failed data lanes that can be tolerated is 3. One completely good quadrant of 5 working lanes must be clear for data transmission.

All tracking of dropped lanes, supported quadrant combinations, and final link width is handled on a per-direction basis for each Intel QPI link pair. This means that each direction of a link pair may be running at different link widths, based on the state of their data lanes. This flexibility allows the system to continue to operate at the maximum available bandwidth possible under the failure conditions.

For analysis of width reduction cases, status registers are used to indicate the status of lanes that have been mapped out, the final negotiated width of the link, and what quadrants are in use. A transmitter-specific register provides the status of detected lane terminations on the transmit side of the link, while a receiver-specific register indicates the status of lanes on the received side as to whether they are active or have been marked as Lane-Dropped during the training process. A width capability register indicates the quadrant combinations that the local component can support, while the link width status register captures the supported widths transmitted by the remote agent and the ultimate link configuration that the local receiver decided on. This information, provided in defined registers, permits software to analyze failures of lanes on a link for diagnostic and debug purposes. Software can then report the status of the link, to allow the customer to plan for potential repairs at a scheduled maintenance interval.

Clock Failover

The optional clock failover feature for Intel QPI is also referred to as Forwarded Clock Fail-Safe operation. The premise of this mode is to define two of the data lanes on the link that may be used as backup clocks lanes, in the event that the primary clock lane fails. If a platform supports this feature, then data lane 9 is treated as the secondary clock lane, and data lane 10 is treated as the tertiary clock lane. The location of these two lanes is important, as it permits clock fail-safe operation, even if the link is wired in a lane reversed manner, or if the link only implements half of the data lanes.

As discussed in Chapter 3, after the physical layer detects the presence of a remote agent during the Detect state of the training state machine, the next step is to lock on to the forwarded clock, which is the basis of data transfer timing. The local port sends the forwarded clock signal on the detected clock lane with highest priority. Thus, if the primary clock lane does not detect termination during the first portion of the Detect state, the local port begins transmission of the clock on lane 9. Remember that an Intel QPI link is managed in quadrants of 5 data lanes each. In the case where either the secondary or tertiary clock lane is used, the quadrant that contains that lane will be unavailable for data transmission, reducing the available data width of the link. Table 6.2 shows the implications on the maximum link width under clock fail-safe operation.

Table 6.2   Clock Fail Safe Mode Link Detection Changes

Normal Link Mode Width	Clock Fail- Safe Mode Width
20 Lanes	10 Lanes
10 Lanes	5 Lanes
5 Lanes	NA

It should be noted that clock fail-safe operation is managed independently for the transmit and receive sides of a link pair, in the same way that data lane failures are handled. This means that one direction of the link pair may be operating at full data width with its primary clock lane, while the other direction is in a reduced data width with a secondary or tertiary clock lane in operation.

Also in the same way that data lane status is recorded in architected registers, clock fail-safe information is also recorded. A physical layer status register in each component tracks which clock lane is in use on the link for both the transmit and receive directions.

Viral Indication

The Viral alert type is a mechanism to indicate an error where it is difficult to avoid error propagation without immediately shutting down the system. Viral alert addresses the error propagation issue for errors not contained to data flits, and allows a system to be shutdown gracefully and in the process to clean up the system interface and other shared resources across system partitions. The viral alert capability of the Intel QuickPath Interconnect is an optional feature that may not be supported by all components and platforms.

The viral signaling is done via a bit in every protocol layer message. Upon reception of a message with the viral indication set an end point will tag the viral indication on all messages sent on all outgoing links. When asserted, the viral mechanism signals that the viral packet is suspect and can no longer be trusted. Viral signaling is appropriate when the scope of the error is at a packet level and not at the data flit level. The viral propagation mechanism is primarily a containment mechanism and not an error signaling mechanism. The viral source end point will independently trigger the appropriate error interrupt and indicate the severity level appropriate for that particular error condition. This allows the flexibility to use the viral containment mechanism for both fatal and nonfatal error conditions.

Upon reception of an Intel QPI packet header with the viral indication set (on any link), the system I/O modules should try to protect the system image in the disk subsystem. This ensures that nonvolatile storage is protected from errors that occur on any component in the system. In addition, this mechanism removes any requirement to bring down the system in a certain amount of time before an error on one component can spread to nonvolatile storage, such as a disk drive.

Data Poisoning

As previously described in Chapter 3, the typical 64-byte data transfer appears on the Intel QPI link as a 9-flit packet. This data transfer has a single header flit (and the header carries the viral indication discussed in the previous section). The other 8 flits carry the 64-byte cache line. This packet structure is depicted in Figure 6.1. Each data flit carries 8 bytes. In addition to the 8 bytes of data the data flit carries a "Poison" indication. The data poisoning indication is a mechanism to indicate that there is an uncorrected data error corresponding just to this specific data flit. In other words, poison indicates a problem with the data content, whereas viral indicates a problem with the link integrity. Data poisoning indication returned in the result of a core-initiated read transaction typically forces a local machine check abort at the initiating processor. By limiting the error signaling to a local machine check abort rather than a global machine check abort, the operating system has the opportunity to recover by killing the affected process rather than killing the whole machine, thus improving system availability.

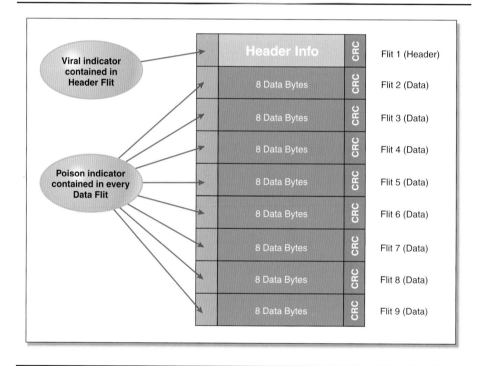

Figure 6.1   Typical 9-Flit Cache Line Data Packet Format

Note   *Unlike viral, poison indicates that just these specific 8 bytes are invalid (this is usually caused by an uncorrectable error indication due to a memory access). Reception of poison data is not an indication of an issue with the system interconnect technology and therefore the system interconnect operation can be assumed to be correct and trusted.*

Timeouts

The Intel QuickPath Architecture provides a definition of a transaction timeout and a hierarchy of timeout levels in order to improve service-ability by providing information useful for properly identifying a failing component. First a transaction timeout is an indication that a component has failed somewhere along the entire transaction path, and in some cases no other error is logged to identify the cause of the failure. The transaction timeout is used to indicate that a transaction has not received all its expected responses within the time period allocated for the transaction. In this case the forwarded request for a transaction fails to complete in its allocated time, then appropriate information is recorded in the error logs at the forwarding entity, and a response with Failed response status (in the Intel QPI response packet) is sent to the requester entity of the transaction.

The timeout of a request at the source of a transaction removes it from the list of outstanding transactions and lets other dependent operations proceed. In case of timeout of a transaction initiated by a core entity, it results in a local machine check abort at the processor. If the transaction is initiated from a non-core entity, then the entity may generate an MCA message or PMI/SMI to one of the cores, go viral, or assert another radial error signal.

Once a packet is dropped, a system will typically experience a cascade of other packets getting dropped or stuck in a buffer, causing an avalanche of transaction timeouts across the system. The solution on Intel QPI to identifying the failed component is to break different packet types into different classes and provide different timeout values per class based on the natural packet dependencies in the protocol. This helps ensure that the first transaction to time out will be related to the original source of the error. This improves serviceability by improving the accuracy of diagnostic firmware used to identify the faulty component.

For interoperability, if all components in the system topology do not support the transaction timeout feature, then this feature should be disabled across the system.

Hot Plug Capabilities

The Intel QPI requirements do not specify a connector, and therefore do not address the physical attributes required to fully support hot plug operations of Intel QPI components. That said, the Intel QPI physical and link layers do provide the functional support needed for online (also referred to as software or logical) addition and deletion of modules, as well as hot plug and removal. This allows system developers to make their own choices as to the level of modularity and hot plug support that is designed into their products.

From the physical layer point of view, the key control bits are the PhyInit-Begin and Reset Modifier controls in the physical layer control register. The Reset Modifier bit allows a software generated reset of a link to override state that is typically "sticky" across soft resets, which pushes the link back to a power-on like state. This is critical to reinitializing with a remote component that has just been added to the system. The PhyInitBegin bit controls the advancement of the state machine into initialization. When PhyInitBegin is deasserted, and the link enters Reset, it will stay in the Reset state in a port disabled manner. This allows hot plug of a remote component without side effects on the existing component's state machine. When the PhyInitBegin control is asserted, the state machine is then allowed to advance to the Detect state to begin the initialization sequence. Software that is involved with the hot plug process will set this bit when the state of the new component is appropriate for detection by the existing system.

For the link layer, the key support provided for hot plug is the ability to perform a reset of the link layer from a software available bit in a link layer control register. This places the link layer back into a state similar to how it existed when the component first powered up. Hardware such as the retry buffer, credit status, CRC mode, and Parameter Exchange information are all reset, and the link layer prepares to perform Parameter Exchange again with the newly added component, once the physical layer has trained and reached the L0 state.

These Intel QPI features are key to enabling functionality for hot plug, but by no means are they the only features necessary. The full array of electrical, logical, and physical features needed to achieve hot plug for a particular set of components, and the exact flow by which those features are used, is left up to each product's implementation.

Dynamic Reconfiguration

In Chapter 5 we discussed dynamic reconfiguration as it related to online addition/removal as well as support of dynamic partitioning, but there is another reason to use dynamic reconfiguration. That is to increase the availability of a system that contains a failed link.

Suppose you had a system where between every end point there were multiple physical paths. Figure 6.2 depicts such a system assuming the processors support route-through. In the case of a link failure, an alternate path can be chosen to connect the agents. Some of those pathways are better than others. Then assume that a single link fails. The system administrator uses the following flow to keep the system up and running:

- Initial failure recovery relies on the routers and the use of VN1 credits to reroute around the failures (during this phase the system administrator requires no intervention). The system relies on the redundant routing information to operate through this failure.

- Quiesces the systems (draining all outstanding transactions).

- Updates the route tables; eliminating the failed link from all routes.

- Optionally "turns off" the failed link.

- Unquiesces the system. Traffic resumes using the new route path.

In this example, note there was no loss of memory, I/O, or processing capacity. There is only a loss of some portion of the total system interconnect bandwidth. In this example, if the system is not using the entire system bandwidth the end users will not perceive any degraded performance.

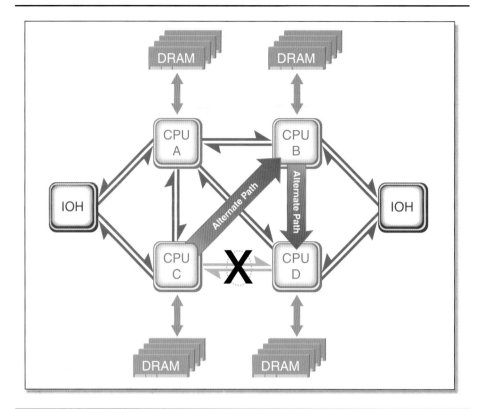

Figure 6.2   Alternate Routing Example

Link Layer DFx Hooks

The Intel QPI link layer has defined a flexible packet framework for the specific purpose of debug and testability. With the shift from a single point of observability with the Front Side Bus to a distributed interconnect with Intel QPI, along with the consolidation of traditional chipset components onto the processor die, challenges arise due to time correlation of information across links and visibility of events occurring between integrated components.

Debug Packets

The Intel QPI link layer provides up to 32 debug message encodings, but currently only 3 are defined, while 29 are reserved for future use. The defined types are the Generic Debug Packet, the Inband Debug Event packet, and the Timing Correlation Packet. The definition of each is discussed below. Each of these is defined within the special class of packets that are link layer only, meaning they are not passed on directly to the upper layers and they do not participate in the recovery process through link level retry. In general, these packets are also unidirectional on the link, in that they do not have a defined response or completion handshake. They can be thought of as "fire and forget" messages that are used to send out information useful for debug, but are not required for normal system operation.

Generic Debug Packets

Generic Debug Packets are intended for providing debug information on an opportunistic basis where link traffic and behavior should not be disturbed. The result of this is that these packets are typically only sent across the link in place of a NULL flit, meaning the link layer has no other information that it needs to pass at the time. Examples of data that might be sent in these packets would be non-timing critical microarchitectural information or performance monitoring data. The single flit packet format provides 55 bits of debug payload, which is defined by each component's implementation.

Inband Debug Event Packets

Inband Debug Event Packets are defined for sending debug related events and values from an Intel QPI device to another device on the other end of the link or possibly to debug tools observing the link. Unlike Generic Debug Packets, it is expected that the Inband Debug Events will be sent with as low a latency as possible, to optimize their relevance for debug. In general, these packets will preempt most packet types except for those used in link level retry scenarios, Parameter Exchange, or Power State control. Component designers should take care, however, to ensure that these packets do not starve out other traffic.

The single flit packet includes a 16-bit event field, which is used in a one-hot manner to encode "pulses" of the debug events that have accumulated while forming the message. Two 18-bit value fields are also provided for exposing internal values. The exact definition of the events and values exposed is left up to each component, but it is suggested that the enabling of events and the placement of their signal and values within the fields be programmable, to minimize the risk of interoperability problems.

The link layer or debug device receiving these packets needs to decode the transmitted events, and then apply them, based on debug control registers, to internal debug event logic for use in triggering, stimulus, or other component defined debug features. Likewise, any transmitted values need to be decoded at the receiver according to the configuration at the transmitting device, before application to the receiving device's debug logic.

Timing Correlation Packets

The final defined debug packet type is a Timing Correlation Packet, also known as a Debug Relative Timing Exposure Packet. These single flit packets are used for exposing device-relative timestamps for later correlation by debug post-processing software. This feature requires various hardware capabilities in the component sending the packets. These include a common timestamp source across all links on a single component, a mechanism for counting the interval since the transmission of the last timing packet, a transmission mechanism for opportunistically replacing NULL flits with these packets, and a transmission mechanism for preemptively scheduling these packets when the maximum interval has elapsed.

An 18-bit Transmit Timing Signature field is provided for encoding the transmit timestamp and phase of transfer information for the issuing of the timing packet. Phase of transfer information is critical where the link layer and physical layer interfaces are running at different clock speeds, thus necessitating information on the phase alignment that the flit was transmitted. For the timestamp, Intel QPI requires a minimum width of 10 bits, to allow enough encoding for both receive and transmit signatures.

Two fields are also provided for sending information relative to the last received timing packet at the link layer. An 18-bit field records the timestamp and phase when the last timing packet was received at the link layer. The lowest order 16 bits of the Transmit Timing Signature field encoded in that received packet is reflected back in the RcvdID field, allowing debug software to know for which packet timing information is being reflected.

Credit Status and Defeaturing

As discussed in Chapter 3, normal link layer flow control on Intel QPI links is managed with credits that are exchanged at initialization time, then decremented by the transmitter on packet transmission and incremented on refund from the remote agent. As such, information and control over credit values is critical for debug and testing of a link. The Intel QuickPath Architecture has provided mechanisms for these areas.

A link layer status register contains defined fields that give status on available credits counts for use in transmission of packets. A snapshot is taken at the point of the register read across all of the Intel QPI–defined credit pools for that link. This includes per virtual channel status for both the VN0 and the VN1 networks, as well as for the shared VNA pool.

For testability, a link layer control register has defined bits that can be used to reduce the number of VNA credits, as well as VN0 and VN1 credits across the virtual channels. Reducing the number of credits can be useful to component design and validation teams for working around problems related to overflowing of queues, as well as reducing the total number of packets that are flowing through the Intel QPI fabric at one time. It should be noted that because credits are only exchanged immediately after Parameter Exchange completes, setting of the credit defeaturing controls will only take effect if done before the link is initially trained or if a link layer soft reset is triggered.

Physical Layer DFx Hooks

Due to the nature of Intel QPI links, which require execution of a state machine through numerous states before any packets can be passed between components, the inclusion of a set of common features for testing and debugging is critical. There is an array of features in this area that cover the analog, clock, and digital portions of the physical layer. The following sections provide an overview of some of these key features.

Compliance State

The Compliance state provides the lowest level of debug and test functionality for the physical layer. It is targeted at diagnosing a nonfunctional link and for measuring severe signal integrity issues such as jitter or noise.

The Compliance state can be entered in one of two ways. The first is in a forced manner through software setting the appropriate bits in a physical layer control register. In this mode, the physical layer will either be configured as a master or a slave device. In the master mode, pattern generator hardware that exists in the physical layer can be configured by software, using register accesses, to transmit programmed patterns down detected data lanes. Upon entering the compliance state in master mode, pattern generation will start according to configuration in a test pattern generator control register. In slave mode, the port will act in a loopback manner, transmitting received data back out to the receive side of the original transmitter.

The second manner of entering the Compliance state is the Auto Compliance mechanism, which causes a transition from the initial portion of the Detect state to Compliance. As mentioned before, the first step in the training state machine is determining the presence of a remote component. If proper termination is detected on the clock lane only, the state machines advances to locking on to the forwarded clock, assuming the remote component is another Intel QPI physical layer. If termination is detected on the clock lane and on any data lanes, the state machine will assume that the remote component is a passive probe, and will advance to Compliance, marking those data lanes with detected terminations as enabled for pattern testing. Entering Compliance in this manner places the port into the equivalent of the forced master mode discussed above, enabling the pattern generation hardware according to its configuration. This then allows laboratory type measurements, using a test setup as shown in Figure 3.7, to be performed on the transmitted signals.

Loop Back

The Compliance methodology discussed above helps debug a single component, and potentially the interconnect between that component and the probe, but this doesn't represent the final topology of the link when two Intel QPI components are involved. With both components installed and operating at full speed, direct probing becomes difficult, making the validation of the link between them problematic. In particular, adding probes to a link operating at speed can disturb the operation of that link and make any measurements suspect. To aid in determining if a link is functional, and if not, to allow for some degree of diagnosis, Intel QPI components provide multiple loopback options.

The loopback function can be done in different ways and at different points in the transmitter and receiver paths in a link pair between two components. The main motivation for the support of multiple modes chosen for Intel QPI was to allow isolation of the transmitter and receiver circuits. To this end there are three defined modes of loopback at each device/link interface, these being:

■ Digital Far End Loopback (DFE-LB) - In this mode data received on the receiver of the Near-end entity is synchronized, deskewed and retimed before being sent back to the transmitter of the same Near-end entity. This loopback mode will be the most widely used method of loopback for most of the test scenarios.

■ Digital Near End loopback (DNE-LB) - In this mode data on the transmit path from the link layer is looped back to the receive path in the link layer. This happens without any interaction with any of the analog circuits of the physical layer including the transmitter and receiver front ends. This type of mode is useful for testing data paths and clock boundary crossings that may exist between the link layer and the physical layer.

■ External Loopback (E-LB) - In this mode the analog voltage signal from the transmitter of the Near end entity is provided a physical path on the Test Interface Unit (TIU) and connected back to a receiver on the Near end entity.

Figure 6.3 depicts the three loop back modes.

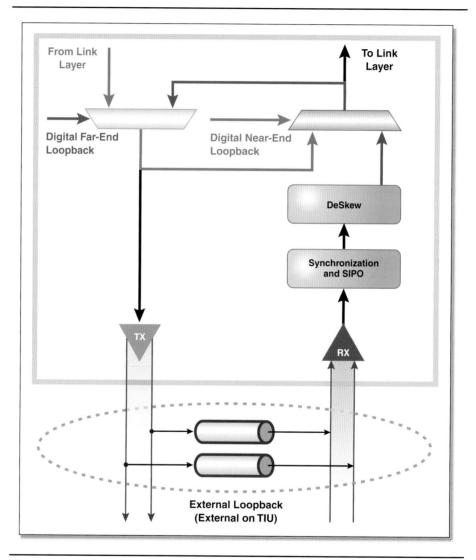

Figure 6.3   Loopback Option Comparisons.

In addition to defining which of the three loopback modes is to be used, one should also define if the particular link interface is the master or the slave. During power up the link layers are configured at the Near-end and

Far-end entities as either a master or a slave. All loopback tests are performed with the master configured entity supporting the pattern generation, results comparison, and error detection functions.

Remote loopback is a loopback path between different Intel QPI devices. In this configuration, one device functions as a loopback master, and the other as a loopback slave. The components advance through a portion of the initialization state machine, to a sub-state within the Polling state. At this point the agent configured as the master indicates its intention to enter the Loopback state, with the slave component acknowledging its intent to enter Loopback as a slave. The master device, once in Loopback, transmits data from the hardware pattern generator. The slave component receives this data, and retransmits it back to the master, who then checks the pattern for errors.

For a single device, there are two possible configurations; these being local intra-link and local inter-link. Figure 6.4 depicts the three possible variants of external loopback testing for Intel QPI devices. Local inter-link requires a connection between two different physical layer ports on the component. With local intra-link loopback there is no slave entity. In this case, the link layer is configured in the master mode and the transmitters and receivers are looped back to each other.

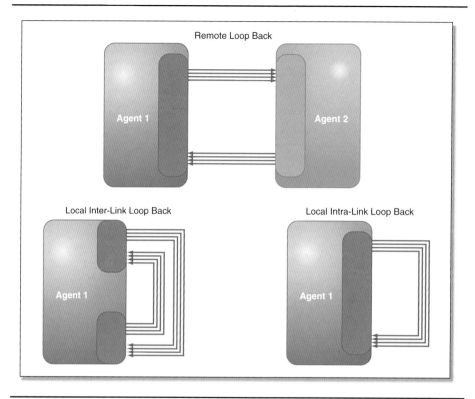

Figure 6.4 Supported External Loopback configurations.

Freeze on Initialization Abort

Default operation of the Intel QPI physical layer state machine when encountering a failure is to return to the Reset state and reattempt initialization. While this is the desired behavior for normal operation, a state machine that is continually cycling through the failure point is difficult to debug and analyze. To aid in debug of these situations, a mode called Freeze on Init Abort can be enabled in a physical layer control register. Enabling this mode will cause the state machine, on detection of a failure that requires a return to the Reset state, to set the State Machine Hold bit in the a previous initialization status register, which stops the state machine at the point of failure. This then allows software to access several status registers that exist in the physical layer in order to determine the state where the failure is occurring, as well as other frozen state information that is relevant to debug. When debug has completed on the port, software can clear the State Machine Hold bit, which will return the port to the Reset state and cause it to begin initialization again. It is also important to note that any Inband Reset that is communicated across the link from a remote component is ignored while the hold bit is asserted.

State Machine Single Step

In addition to freezing the state machine to allow debug, a single step mode exists to allow experiments and workarounds to be applied to a port. Enabling of single step mode is controlled by a bit in a physical layer control register. When asserted, the state machine begins single stepping the next time that a soft reset occurs.

The single step functionality works by gating the exit of a state in the state machine, and thus the entering of the next state, even if all exit criteria have been met. The Single Step Hold bit is asserted in a previous initialization status register when exit has been gated. By clearing this bit, software can advance the state machine to the end of the next state, before the bit again asserts and state exit is stopped. Note there are a limited number of states into which Single Step cannot block advancement. When Single Step is enabled, the secondary timers that are used to detect a timeout condition in a state are disabled, effectively being replaced by the hold bit.

By stopping the state machine at the end of each state, software can read out the status of the port to determine the failure or success of the state whose exit has been stopped. Also, if permitted by the design of the component, overrides for port state that may have been incorrectly set can be applied, as a method of working around problems.

Latency Fixing

One of the operations that occurs in the physical layer as part of the initialization state machine is the deskewing of data across received lanes. After a link has reached L0, the state of deskew settings will not change, so the latency across the link from remote link layer to local link layer will remain the same. After another initialization of the same link however, it is possible that the deskew operation will result in a different latency. For repeating test content on the same part, and across multiple parts, this variability may pose a challenge. To address this, Intel QPI defines a Latency Fixing operation using a structure known as the Latency Buffer.

At a high level, the purpose of the Latency Buffer is to provide additional delay into the interface between the physical layer and link layer, to normalize for any variations caused by different deskew results. Parameters in the physical layer are programmed that represent the Target Latency for the link. During training, the physical layer computes the actual latency that exists on the link for the current initialization, and then uses slots available in the Latency Buffer to add any required bit time delays to meet the programmed Target Latency. By selecting a Target Latency value that is larger than the maximum value that will occur due to the normal training of the link across initializations and across parts, consistent link latency will exist for each test run. It should be noted that the Latency Buffer achieves normalization by adding delay into the link, so a Target Latency should be picked that is larger than the actual latency of the link.

Debug Tools and Examples

Conventional debug and probing techniques generally are not applicable given the sensitive high speed analog blocks that deliver flits at the Intel QPI transfer rates. In addition direct probing of an Intel QPI link could prove to be a physical challenge due to PCB routing and layout constraints. To that end the Intel QuickPath Architecture has made provisions for repeater-based probing as well as debug and analysis of the high speed analog blocks.

Probing

With transfer rates on Intel QPI links starting at a minimum of 4.8 GT/s, it is no longer possible to probe a signal using the same methods that existed with FSB technology, as these would inject too much noise or jitter, making the lane or lanes unusable. This statement thus raises the question, how do you observe the traffic on a link without bringing down the link?

To deal with this problem, the physical layer has been architected with support for repeater-based observability technology in mind. There are four types of repeaters comprehended by the architecture.

The first type, called a Re-sample type, only affects the voltage of the link as it repeats the signal, but doesn't affect jitter or drift between the components. While defined as a type of repeater, these are currently not supported.

The Re-sync and Deskew types of repeaters are components that sit inline between the two physical layers, sampling and retransmitting the data to obtain observability. The Re-sync type of repeater has a drift buffer, thus resetting jitter and drift between the components. The Deskew type of repeater goes the additional step of deskewing the data as it samples it. This deskewing incurs an additional latency in the path to the receiver component.

The final type of repeater isn't a true repeater at all. The Non-Physical Layer type essentially constitutes an independent port on a component that is explicitly used for mirroring the traffic that is occurring on one of the component's links. The behavior of the true link can then be observed through this port, preventing any disruption in the path of the true link or any type of socket interposer or probe point on the board. These types of ports are not covered by the overall architecture, leaving their design to individual components.

Overall, repeaters should ensure the following

■ No flits are added or removed from the link. From the link layer points of view, the flit traffic should not change from transmitting link layer to receiving link layer.

■ Repeaters are defined for one direction of a link pair only. Observing a full Intel QPI link-pair will take two repeaters, which should operate independently from each other.

■ The repeater should preserve all physical layer training parameters unchanged during initialization.

■ The repeater should pass inband reset indications on to the downstream component, but should not induce an inband reset on its own.

One of the primary considerations when designing an Intel QPI component with probing in mind is to allow for the additional latency that a repeater introduces. With additional latency, the sizing of structures like the link level retry Buffer and Packet/Credit Pools becomes important to ensure that traffic continues to flow without disruption due to the filling of these structures. Likewise, timeout counters in the physical layer need to allow for the additional time that will be spent in each state of the initialization state machine.

An Intel QPI repeater device has been created to be available for use in debug and observability of the first generation of Intel QPI components. This repeater device is part of test and debug solutions from companies that have developed specific probing solutions for each of the first generation Intel QPI components designed by Intel. The reader is encouraged to contact their preferred test equipment supplier, or Intel Corporation, for more information on Intel QPI probing solutions. Below is a brief description of some of the general probing topologies that have been produced.

Repeaters—Socket Interposer and Mid-Bus Topologies

Where to place a repeater in a system raises some interesting options with Intel QPI–based systems. With the FSB, the observation points were at the component sockets, by placing an interposer in between the processor and the socket on the board. For Intel QPI, because the link is point to point rather than the shared signaling of a bus, a repeater can be placed anywhere along its length.

One option is to place it near the end points, in a socket interposer type manner similar to FSB. This works by placing the repeater chip on the interposer itself and connecting one side to the processor pins while connecting the other to the socket. Figure 6.5 gives a diagram showing how signals are routed in this case. Figure 6.6 is a photograph of an actual socket interposer probing solution.

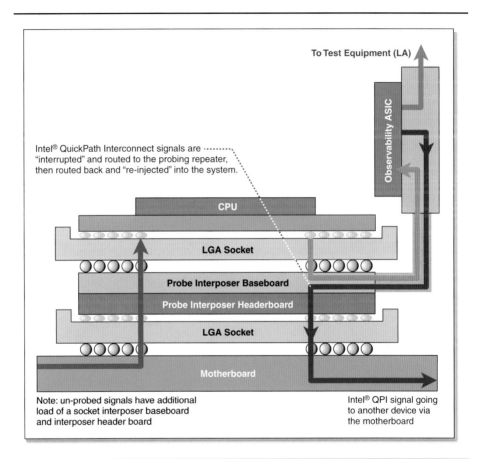

Figure 6.5 Functional Diagram of an Interposer Probing Solution

Photo courtesy of Intel Corporation.

Figure 6.6   A Processor Socket Interposer

This interposer-based probing topology closely mirrors what existed for FSB, but has the added challenge of needing interposers on every socket. This means extra keep-out space between components to allow for the cabling of the interposer.

Another solution that exists is that of the mid-bus probe. This requires a probe point somewhere on the system board where the wires of a link can be "broken," and the repeater inserted. A functional diagram is shown in Figure 6.7 while Figure 6.8 shows a computer aided design drawing of a mid-bus probe device. Figure 6.9 gives a photograph of an actual device.

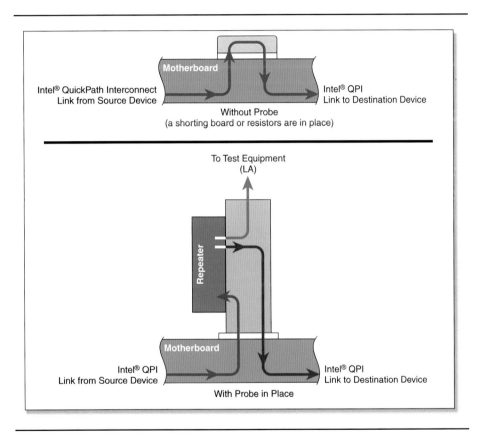

Figure 6.7 Functional Diagram of a Mid-Bus Probing Solution

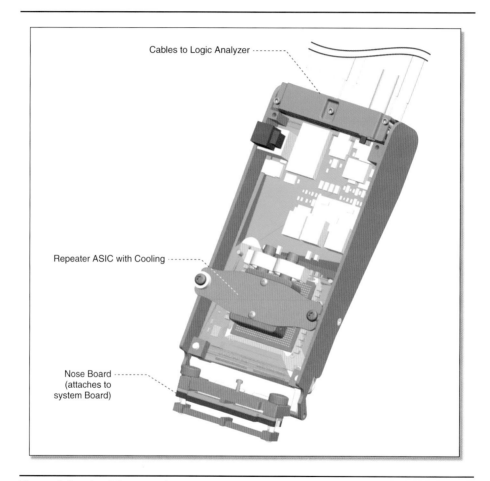

Figure 6.8   A Mid-Bus Probe Diagram

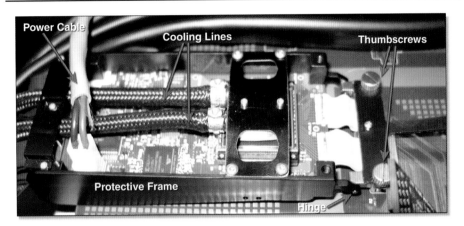

Photo courtesy of Intel Corporation.

Figure 6.9 A Mid-Bus Probe

This mid-bus probing solution has the advantage of physically positioning the probe point on the underside of the system board, outside the clutter of memory, processors, I/O cards, and so on. It does require, however, a method for connecting/disconnecting the lanes of the link when switching from using a repeater back to normal operation.

Visualization and Debug Software—IRIS

To provide a framework to debug systems based on the Intel QuickPath Interconnect a software debug framework was developed, referred to as IRIS. IRIS is an end-to-end software debug framework. IRIS provides a user view into a total system that encompasses the Intel QPI links, as well as DDR3 and Processor "sideband" signals, giving the debug engineer high-level analysis and debug tools. IRIS provides seamless interoperability between tools as well as support for multiple logic analyzers.

The motivations behind IRIS were very simple: To provide a unified debug environment of the system; to reduce cost of training, development and support in the debug lab. It is easy to see that relying on a disjoint tool set that has no common interface simply extends the debug time in the lab. Some features of IRIS are:

- Capture/display external traces: This means providing logic analyzer trigger, filter, and run controls.
- Program microarchitecture debug features: High level GUI and ability to extract microarchitecture state for post processing.
- Correlation/analysis capabilities: Transaction and data correlation between links and other interfaces {(Intel QPI, DDR3, PCIe, and so on.
  - IRIS is capable of "stitching" Intel QPI packets/frames together to form a representation of a complete transaction. This information can be displayed as a flow or Feynman diagram, for a given link, or from a given socket perspective.
- Ruling checking
  - Intel QPI syntax/semantic rules
  - Intel QPI link layer rules
  - Intel QPI coherent and non-coherent protocol layer rules
  - PCIe/memory interface rules
- Support for multiple logic analyzer suppliers.

Several examples of the graphical user interface of IRIS are contained in the Figures 6.10 through 6.12. Figure 6.10 shows the user interface of a fully instrumented four-processor socket configuration. Figures 6.11 and 6.12 provide the user with information flowing over several Intel QPI links of the system.

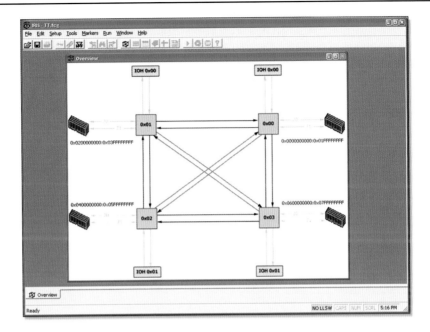

Figure 6.10 IRIS Main Panel Representation of a Four Processor System

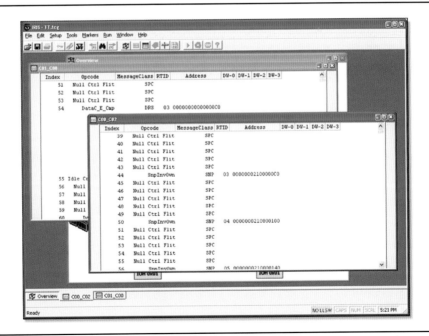

Figure 6.11 Intel® QuickPath Interconnect Packet Listing Panel for a Given Link Direction

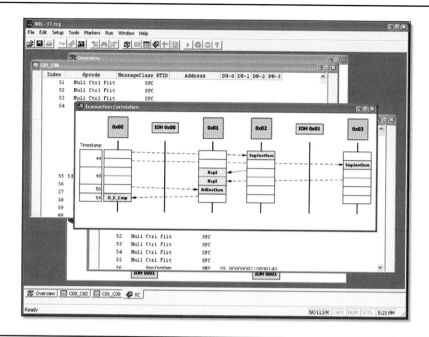

Figure 6.12 Transaction Correlation of a Coherent Transaction via a Feynman Diagram Representation across Four Processor Sockets

In System Link Margining

At the signaling speeds involved with Intel QuickPath Interconnect links, any measurement point other than inside the receiver of the device will not be assured to be an accurate representation of what the receiver will actually sample. What is needed is a method for performing such measurements at speed, within the system configuration that the devices must operate in. Devices designed to the requirements of the Intel QuickPath Architecture therefore contain the hooks needed to enable this form of testing. These hooks include the ability to generate, loopback, and check test patterns being sent across the links. They also include the ability to modify certain transmitter and receiver characteristics so that a range of operating conditions can be covered and the link can be tested to determine at what point failures could start to occur.

ASSET InterTech, Inc. has collaborated with Intel Corporation to create a product known as the Scanworks† IBIST Toolkit. This toolkit can control the execution of tests on several interfaces including Intel QPI. It does this by exercising the built-in pattern generation and checking functions of the devices. User-defined patterns or component-created pseudo-random patterns can be driven and checked at the full operating speed of the link. This is done under the same interconnect channel characteristics that the platform will use in normal operation. No additional probing is added to the link circuits. The toolkit works by accessing functions of the devices through the JTAG test access port. With this pattern generation and checking testing, the link's basic connectivity and data integrity can be checked.

For more in-depth bit error rate (BER) testing, the toolkit can keep track of the total bits transferred and the total error count. This allows a computation of the observed BER for that link. Furthermore, the toolkit can modify equalization settings at the transmitter, and introduce voltage and timing offsets at the receiver while the tests are underway. In this manner the tool can build up a representation of the received data eye diagram—at speed and in system. This allows the user to identify relative receiver performance margins for the platform under test. A sample of such an eye diagram is shown as Figure 6.13.

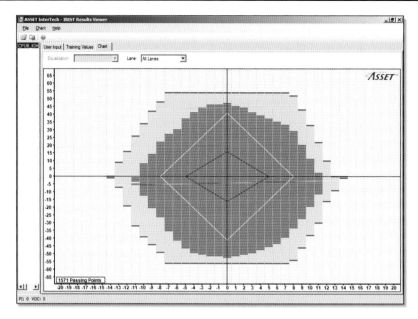

Photo Courtesy of ASSET InterTech.

Figure 6.13 Scanworks[†] Generated Eye Diagram

The toolkit itself executes on a host PC system, interconnected to the system under test through a USB cable connecting to the JTAG bus on the target machine. All devices connected to that JTAG bus can be controlled through this interface. Figure 6.14 shows a typical host and target configuration. For more information on the Scanworks[†] toolkit, please see http://www.asset-intertech.com/ or contact ASSET InterTech, Inc. directly.

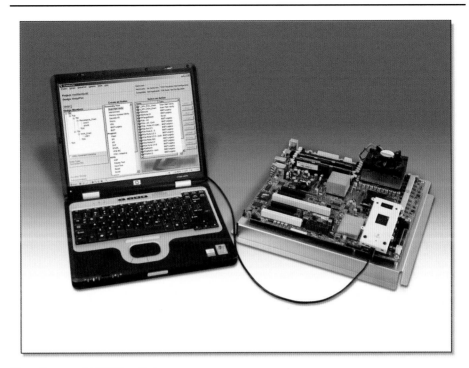

Photo Courtesy of ASSET InterTech.

Figure 6.14 Typical Scanworks† Toolkit Setup

Summary

This chapter has described in general terms how the RAS and DFx features employed in larger systems can be accomplished in a system topology based on the Intel QuickPath Interconnect. These features enable complex system functions and the detection and toleration of errors providing a reliable and robust interconnect topology.

Epilogue

Prediction is very difficult, especially about the future.

—Niels Bohr (1885–1962)

The goal of this book is to enhance the reader's understanding of the Intel®
Quickpath Interconnect (Intel QPI). You are invited go to this book's
companion Web page at www.intel.com/intelpress/qpi for a digital edition of
the book, training information and live reference links.

The Intel QuickPath Interconnect is the system interconnect used by Intel
server processors starting with the Intel® Xeon® 5500 introduced in 2009.
This new interface was designed to replace the Front Side Bus (FSB) which
has been the long running standard interface for Intel processors since the
Pentium® Pro processor was introduced in 1994. The FSB, a common shared
system bus, seamlessly ties together multiple processors, I/O devices, and a
single memory controller. The Intel QuickPath Interconnect provides a new
system foundation which maximizes the potential of future generations of
microprocessors.

Intel QPI delivers high bandwidth with a low latency by providing
direct high speed links between processors, *multiple* memory controllers,
and I/O devices. Multi-processor systems that are fully connected with Intel
QPI links offer the lowest latency and can deliver very high performance.
All these links operate in parallel providing very high throughput in the

system. However such a system based upon multiple links makes it challenging to manage coherence among multiple caches in the system. The two-hop, source snoop behavior with cache line forwarding offers the fastest request completion in smaller scale mainstream systems, while the home snoop behavior allows for optimizing highly scalable servers. Intel QPI provides the robust error detection and correction attributes that enable reliable operation of the interconnect. This total set of performance and features has made Intel QPI very compelling for system designers.

In Chapter 2 we provided an extensive view into the operations that can be performed over the Intel Quickpath Interconnect. These operations are used in systems based on either the IA-32 architecture or the Intel® Itanium® processors. The details of the flow of messages and their interactions in systems with two or more processor provide insights into how Intel QPI efficiently handles and manages cache coherence in such systems. Interrupts and other system control messages are handled in a manner that is compatible with their operation in prior generation systems so that they are entirely transparent to any software that runs on Intel QPI based systems.

The Intel QuickPath Architecture is a layered approach not unlike that of a communications protocol. The individual layers behave and operate relatively autonomously, encapsulating the specific functions they perform and providing a systematic interface to the higher levels of the architecture. Chapter 3 presented the details of the physical and link layers and how they work together to enable components to communicate with each other in order to support the higher level flow of messages. The physical layer was designed to ease the challenges of a system designer when laying out the traces of the very high speed signals of Intel QPI links. The circuits in this layer compensate for timing skews between signals on the Intel QPI lanes to remove most bit level synchronization issues. The transmitters and receivers also compensate for electrical losses in the channels between the devices through equalization, thereby allowing devices to transfer high speed data properly across relatively long interconnects. The link layer was shown to be responsible for delivering messages and data across the links of Intel QPI in a reliable manner. Details of how the link layer can present virtual channels and different message classes to the higher layers of Intel QPI were described, as were the mechanisms employed to ensure that packets are delivered to the receiver free of errors.

In order for a system using Intel QPI to operate correctly, all the devices in a system must be setup with the proper information regarding the configuration of the system. Chapter 4 covered the process of getting the myriad of hardware resources properly initialized so that real work can then be performed by the system. The interaction of boot firmware with the hardware was discussed, beginning with the basic steps of getting links operational, moving on to discovering the different Intel QPI resources in the system in a methodical manner, assigning Node IDs, handing control over to the boot agent at the appropriate point, and eventually proceeding through to memory initialization.

We explored some of the higher-level capabilities of systems based on the Intel QuickPath Architecture in Chapter 5. This chapter described in general terms how several complex system functions employed in larger systems can be accomplished in a platform based on the Intel QuickPath Interconnect. We describe how Intel QPI supports dynamic system reconfiguration and provides features for large multiprocessor systems to be partitioned to run more than one operating system instance independent of each other. These partitions can be created dynamically, permitting a system to be reconfigured to serve very diverse needs.

Intel QPI offers several features required to build robust systems that have a certain amount of fault resilience. In Chapter 6 we explored how the Intel QuickPath Interconnect not only provides a high performance interface for enabling these sort of system functions, but it also has provisions to detect and tolerate errors, making for a more reliable and robust interconnect. We described how the RAS and DFx features employed in larger systems can be accomplished in a system topology based on the Intel QuickPath Interconnect. These features enable complex system functions and the detection and toleration of errors providing a reliable and robust interconnect topology.

Futures

The Intel Quickpath Interconnect has been architected with headroom for expansion and extension in the future. In addition, the individual layers of the architecture have also been designed with expandability in mind. At this point we can only speculate on some of the possible ways in which these capabilities can be used in the future systems. These are mere speculations of the authors designed to illustrate the extensibility architected into this new system fabric. They should not be construed in any way to represent any product plans of Intel Corporation.

The layered architecture of Intel QPI lends itself well to making significant upgrades through the replacement of an entire layer, while keeping the layers above and below unchanged. For example, the current physical layer of Intel QPI is designed to transfer data over electrical signals, specifically copper wiring on printed circuit boards. This layer is entirely self-contained and in the future could be replaced by one that uses optical media or other suitable high speed interconnect. The digital and analog sub-blocks of today's physical layer would be redesigned accordingly to take advantage of the capabilities of the new signaling technology. The rest of the layers of the Intel Quickpath Interface, including the messaging content, would be unaffected by such a change.

The various layers have been architected with headroom for future extensions. As an example new virtual channels, additional messages, and packet types can be readily added to the existing set supported by the link layer. It is quite possible that Intel QPI would be the interface of choice for future media processors that handle streams of data longer than a typical cache line defined today. The existing link layer has headroom for additional data types that could be used for this purpose. Moreover the interface provides mechanisms to interleave such data streams with other traffic across the physical link without adversely impacting their operation.

Such extensibility is also available in other layers. The routing layer and the cache coherence protocol layer can also be suitably extended to meet the needs of future systems. One example would be smart routing algorithms that could be implemented as part of the routing layer to balance the load across links in larger system configurations.

This new system interconnect offers a set of possibilities that are quite large. With the past track record of innovation as a guide, we expect future Intel QPI device implementation teams to come up with many useful, novel, and remarkably unique ways to use and extend the interface. We will watch their designs with interest.

For More Information

Please visit the Intel Web site, www.intel.com, for the most up-to-date information on all technologies and products offered by Intel that include the Intel Quickpath Interconnect.

Index

Reset Modifier control, 234
Reset state
   description of, 104
   freeze on initialization abort, 244–245
   hot plug capabilities and, 234
   Inband Reset to take link back to, 113
   in physical layer finite state machine, 104
re-silvering process, 203–204
response
   Data/Non-Data responses, 46
   non-Coherent read/write transactions,
      60–63
   snoop, 47, 51–52
   for transaction completion, 46
response data state, 140
Re-sync repeater, 247
retraining
   interval/duration, 143
   periodic, 111
retry buffer
   in link layer retry, 129–131
   outgoing flits saved in, 126
   for recovery, 125
ringing, 96, 97
Rolling CRC
   for bit error detection/recovery, 225
   choice of, 146
   description of, 126–128
route tables, 220, 221
route-through
   dynamic reconfiguration and, 235
   topology discovery and, 169
routing
   communication infrastructure
      programming and, 172–173
   dynamic reconfiguration and, 235–236
   setting, 154
routing layer
   extensibility of, 264
   function of, 26–27
   of Intel QPI, 22
   in transaction flow, 44–45
routing table array (RTA), 172–173

routing tables, of routing layer, 26–27
RRSM (Remote Retry State Machine), 131,
   133
RspStatus=Failed, 214
RTA (routing table array), 172–173
rules
   for assignment of TID/NID, 43–44
   Iris ruling checking, 254
   for memory population, 179
   of snoop operation, 11
   for Write Combining Write/Write
      Combining Write Partial, 62–63

S

SADs. *See* source address decoders
Safranek, Robert J., xvi, xxii
SAG (System Address Gap) registers, 183
SAPIC interrupt architecture
   Intel QPI support of, 65, 217
   interrupt process, 66–67
SBSP. *See* System Bootstrap Processor
scalability, of Intel QPI, 14
scaling, 77–78
Scanworks† IBIST Toolkit, 257–259
scrubbing logic, 195
self-healing
   clock failover, 229–230
   data lane failover, 228–229
sequence number, 131
Serial Presence Detect (SPD) data, 179–180
serviceability
   of Intel QPI, 14
   timeouts for, 233
shared snoop response, 51
Shared state
   description of, 7
   MESI states, 8
   snoop operation and, 10–11
   writing to coherent memory and, 56
signaling
   differential for signal quality, 94
   with FSB, 89
   imperfections, tolerance of, 85

Continuing Education is Essential

It's a challenge we all face – keeping pace with constant change in information technology. Whether our formal training was recent or long ago, we must all find time to keep ourselves educated and up to date in spite of the daily time pressures of our profession.

Intel produces technical books to help the industry learn about the latest technologies. The focus of these publications spans the basic motivation and origin for a technology through its practical application.

Right books, right time, from the experts

These technical books are planned to synchronize with roadmaps for technology and platforms, in order to give the industry a head-start. They provide new insights, in an engineer-to-engineer voice, from named experts. Sharing proven insights and design methods is intended to make it more practical for you to embrace the latest technology with greater design freedom and reduced risks.

I encourage you to take full advantage of Intel Press books as a way to dive deeper into the latest technologies, as you plan and develop your next generation products. They are an essential tool for every practicing engineer or programmer. I hope you will make them a part of your continuing education tool box.

Sincerely,

Justin Rattner
Senior Fellow and Chief Technology Officer
Intel Corporation

Turn the page to learn about titles
from Intel Press for system developers

Mastering High Performance Multiprocessor Signaling

Electrical design with the Intel® QuickPath Interconnect

Dave Coleman and Michael Mirmak

Mastering High Performance Multiprocessor Signaling explains the electrical design, board layout, test & measurement and validation elements involved in implementing the Intel® QuickPath Interconnect, the foundation of future generations of Intel® microprocessor systems, using a high speed, packetized, point-to-point system interconnect that uses multiple narrow high speed differential links to stitch together processors into a fabric of a distributed shared memory-style platform architecture.

Creating circuits for the very high speeds demanded by today's computers require skill sets that are not commonly provided by conventional electrical engineering education. Differential signaling is now the fundamental technology enabling high speed, microwave frequency data rates. Signaling speeds of Intel QuickPath Interconnect are now so high, transmission channel artifacts such as frequency dependent attenuation, ringing and crosstalk will have an influence across several bits of transmitted data.

Mastering High Performance Multiprocessor Signaling is written by Intel experts who explain the new concepts and vocabulary of this new domain and relate their insights and experience, thoroughly explaining each step from design through validation, so that electrical circuit developers can directly apply the information contained here to produce high quality products that meet the demanding time-to-market requirements of the computer industry today.

Active Platform Management Demystified

Unleashing the power of Intel® vPro™ Technology

Arvind Kumar, Purushottam Goel and Ylian Saint-Hilare
ISBN 978-1-934053-19-5

Has your IT organization been hampered by the need for faster, more accurate asset management, reduced downtime with fewer deskside maintenance and repair visits, and improved malware prevention and response?

Would your business benefit from a solution for out-of-band manageability and security when the PC is in a low-power state or even powered off, the operating system is unresponsive, or software agents are disabled?

Active Platform Management Demystified shows how to gain these abilities, and more, by taking advantage of the hardware-assisted security and manageability features in notebook and desktop PCs equipped with Intel® vPro™ technology which is controlled by Intel® Active Management Technology (Intel® AMT). "Active Platform Management Demystified will become an important resource for anyone navigating state-of-the-art management technology." *Winston Bumpus, Distributed Management Task Force president.*

> IT Best Practices Series
>
> Active Platform Management Demystified
>
> Unleashing the power of Intel® vPro™ Technology
>
> By Arvind Kumar, Purushottam Goel, and Ylian Saint-Hilaire
>
> Intel
> PRESS

Arvind Kumar, Purushottam Goel and Ylian Saint-Hilaire give a a complete description of how the features of Intel® AMT can be used to ease the burden of maintaining, managing and protecting PCs in both the Enterprise and Small Business environments. It has something for eveyone connected making computing more secure: "Active Platform Management Demystified provides a good balance between technology overview and implementation details, making it a great book for ISV product teams – including product managers, senior engineers, architects and support personnel." *opines Max Sokolov of Symantec Corp.*

Intel® AMT provides an access point for the latest management consoles from Microsoft*, Altiris*, Cisco*, LANDesk*, HP* and other Independent Software Vendors to allow IT practitioners to take advantage of Intel AMT features in the process of managing computers over a wired or corporate wireless network- or even outside the corporate firewall through a wired LAN connection. "Active Platform Management Demysitfied thoroughly covers the concepts of Intel® vPro™ Technology and does a good job of explaining general system defense issues. Especially valuable is its description of the management of network filters used to identify and remedy potential threats." *Christophe Graham, Hewlett-Packard Technical Strategist*

Dynamics of a Trusted Platform
A Building Block Approach
By David Grawrock
ISBN 978-1-934053-08-9

In Dynamics of a Trusted Platform David Grawrock has updated his highly popular Intel Safer Computing Initiative with new topics covering the latest developments in secure computing. The reader is introduced to the concept of Trusted Computing and the building block approach to designing security into PC platforms. The Intel® Trusted Execution Technology† (Intel® TXT) is one of those building blocks that can be used to create a trusted platform by integrating new security features and capabilities into the processor, chipset, and other platform components.

 "The chapters on Anatomy of an Attack and System Protection present useful, practical information that will help familiarize a person with the impacts of protection (or lack thereof) of system components and resources. Treatment of the topic of measurement is particularly useful for system designers and programmers." - *Amy C Nelson, Dell, Inc*

"David finds analogies in everyday life to clearly explain many of the concepts in this book. I would highly recommended Dynamics of a Trusted Platform for researchers, architects, and designers who are serious about trusted computing." - *Dr. Sigrid Gürgens Fraunhofer Institute for Secure Information Technology (SIT)*

"The opportunity now exists to start building trusted systems, making this book very timely. It would be foolhardy to start without a thorough understanding of the concepts; and this is what Dynamics of a Trusted Platform gives you. The building blocks described here are certainly able to imbue the infrastructure with a higher level of trustworthiness, and we may all look forward to the many benefits flowing from that." - *Andrew Martin Director, Oxford University Software Engineering Centre*

Applied Virtualization Technology

Usage Models for IT Professionals and Software Developers

By Sean Campbell and Michael Jeronimo
ISBN 978-0-976483-26-6

Server and desktop virtualization is one of the more significant technologies to impact computing in the last few years, promising the benefits of infrastructure consolidation, lower costs, increased security, ease of management, and greater employee productivity.

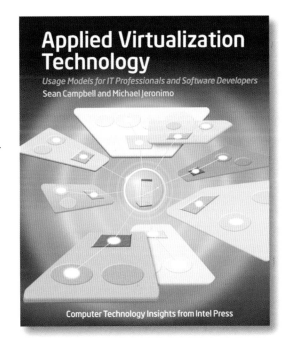

Using virtualization technology, one computer system can operate as multiple "virtual" systems. The convergence of affordable, powerful platforms and robust scalable virtualization solutions is spurring many technologists to examine the broad range of uses for virtualization. In addition, a set of processor and I/O enhancements to Intel server and client platforms, known as Intel® Virtualization Technology (Intel® VT), can further improve the performance and robustness of current software virtualization solutions.

This book takes a user-centered view and describes virtualization usage models for IT professionals, software developers, and software quality assurance staff. The book helps you plan the introduction of virtualization solutions into your environment and thereby reap the benefits of this emerging technology.

Highlights include

- The challenges of current virtualization solutions
- In-depth examination of three software-based virtualization products
- Usage models that enable greater IT agility and cost savings
- Usage models for enhancing software development and QA environments
- Maximizing utilization and increasing flexibility of computing resources
- Reaping the security benefits of computer virtualization
- Distribution and deployment strategies for virtualization solutions

Energy Efficiency for Information Technology

How to Reduce Power Consumption in Servers and Data Centers
By David Grawrock
ISBN 978-1-934053-08-9

Minimizing power consumption is one of the primary technical challenges that today's IT organizations face. In Energy Efficiency for Information Technology, Lauri Minas and Brad Ellison point out, that the overall consumption of electrical power by data centers can be reduced by understanding the several sources of power consumption and minimizing each one. Drawing on their engineering experience within Intel Corporation and with the industry, they break down power consumption into its constituent parts and explain each in a bottom-up fashion. With energy consumption well defined, Minas and Ellison systematically provide guidance for minimizing each draw on electrical power.

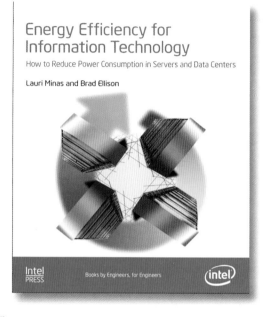

"Throughout my global travels, I hear increasing concern for the issues of power consumption by data centers, both due to the costs and also harm to the planet. *Energy Efficiency for Information Technology* addresses a critical issue for IT suppliers and consumers alike." Vernon Turner, Senior Vice President & General Manager, Enterprise Computing, Network, Consumer, and Infrastructure, IDC

"In *Energy Efficiency for Information Technology* Minas and Ellison underscore the magnitude of increases in power consumption, they systematically suggest ways to minimize consumption and provide checklists and assessments tables that are particularly useful to gather or summarize the right information for the planning. This is a multidimensional book that addresses a serious challenge to IT departments around the globe."
YY Chow, Managing Director, Systems and Securities Services, Mitsubishi-UFJ Securities

"*Energy Efficiency for Information Technology* is a remarkable compilation of cutting-edge technical knowledge for addressing the critical issue of power and cooling in data centers. It shows how your data center can compute more but cost less, while also reducing energy use and environmental impacts". Jonathan Koomey, Ph.D., Project Scientist, Lawrence Berkeley National Laboratory

"Lauri Minas and Brad Ellison have written an important book that explains how diligent IT professionals can maximize the productivity of their data centers while minimizing power costs. These Intel engineers speak from experience and with authority. Anyone seriously interested in the greening of IT should read *Energy Efficiency for Information Technology*." Lorie Wigle, President, Climate Servers Computing Initiative.

Service Oriented Architecture Demystified
A pragmatic approach to SOA for the IT executives
By Girish Juneja, Blake Dournaee, Joe Natoli, and Steve Birkel
ISBN 978-1-934053-02-7

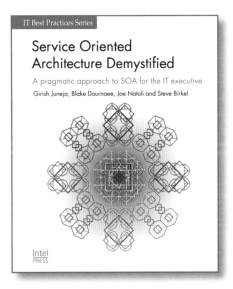

The authors of this definitive book on SOA debunk the myths and demonstrate through examples from different vertical industries how a "crawl, walk, run" approach to deployment of SOA in an IT environment can lead to a successful return on investment.

One popular argument states that SOA is not a technology per se, but that it stands alone and can be implemented using a wide range of technologies. The authors believe that this definition, while attractive and elegant, doesn't necessarily pass pragmatic muster.

Service Oriented Architecture Demystified describes both the technical and organizational impacts of adopting SOA and the pursuant challenges. The authors demonstrate through real life deployments why and how different industry sectors are adopting SOA, the challenges they face, the advantages they have realized, and how they have (or have not) addressed the issues emerging from their adoption of SOA. This book strikes a careful balance between describing SOA as an enabler of business processes and presenting SOA as a blueprint for the design of software systems in general. Throughout the book, the authors attempt to cater to both technical and organizational viewpoints, and show how both are very different in terms of why SOA is useful. The IT software architect sees SOA as a business process enabler and the CTO sees SOA as a technology trend with powerful paradigms for software development and software integration.

SOA can be characterized in terms of different vertical markets. For each such market, achieving SOA means something different and involves different transformational shifts. The vertical markets covered include healthcare, government, manufacturing, finance, and telecommunications. SOA considerations are quite different across these vertical markets, and in some cases, the required organizational shifts and technology shifts are highly divergent and context dependent.

Whether you are a CTO, CIO, IT manager, or IT architect, this book provides you with the means to analyze the readiness of your internal IT organization and with technologies to adopt a service oriented approach to IT.

The Business Value of Virtual Service Oriented Grids

Strategic Insights for Enterprise Decision Makers

By Enrique Castro-leon, Jackson He, Mark Chang and Parviz Peiravi
ISBN 978-1-934053-10-2

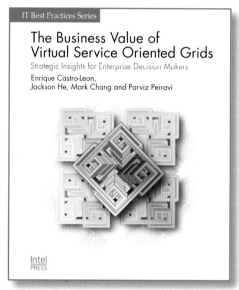

"In this book the authors track the trends, create new rules based on new realities, and establish new market models. With virtual service-oriented grids, the sky is the limit," writes Wei-jen Lee, a University of Texas – Arlington professor, about *The Business Value of Virtual Service Oriented Grids*, a new book published by Intel. The application of service-oriented architecture (SOA) for business will interest application developers looking for the latest advances in technology and ideas on how to utilize those advances to keep up in a global economy. *The Business Value of Virtual Service Oriented Grids* provides a framework that describes how the convergence of three well-known technologies are defining a new information technology model that will fundamentally change the way we do business. The first step, say the authors, is the development of new applications for the consumer market. However, even bigger is the development of new applications in a federated fashion using services modules called *servicelets*. These federated or composite applications can be built in a fraction of the time it takes to develop traditional applications. This new environment will lower the bar for applications development, opening opportunities for thousands of smaller players worldwide.

"We live in exponential times. . . . The economy is now thoroughly global. The Internet has replaced many of the middle layers of business, has enabled many to work from home or from a small company, and is revolutionizing the retail industries." writes Portland State University professor Gerald Sheble.

"The advent of SOA is going to impact information processing and computer services on a scale not previously envisioned." The speed-up in application development and integration will accelerate the deployment of IT capabilities, which in turn will have a consequential effect on the organization's business agility. Corporate decision makers will enjoy the ability to pick and choose among capital and operations expenses to suit their organization's business goals. The book describes the business trends within which this convergence is taking place and provides insight on how these changes can affect your business. It clearly explains the interplay between technology, architectural considerations, and standards with illustrative examples. Finally, the book tells you how your organization can benefit from *servicelets*, alerts you about integration pitfalls, and describes approaches for putting together your technology adoption strategy for building your virtual SOA environment using *servicelets*.

About Intel Press

Intel Press is the authoritative source of timely, technical books
to help software and hardware developers speed up their development
process. We collaborate only with leading industry experts to deliver
reliable, first-to-market information about the latest
technologies, processes, and strategies.

Our products are planned with the help of many people in the developer
community and we encourage you to consider becoming a customer advisor.
If you would like to help us and gain additional advance insight to the latest
technologies, we encourage you to consider the Intel Press Customer
Advisor Program. You can register here:

www.intel.com/intelpress/register.htm

For information about bulk orders or corporate sales, please send e-mail to:
bulkbooksales@intel.com

Other Developer Resources from Intel

At these Web sites you can also find valuable technical information and
resources for developers:

www.intel.com/technology/rr	Recommended reading list for books of interest to developers
www.intel.com/technology/itj	Intel Technology Journal
developer.intel.com	General information for developers
www.intel.com/software	content, tools, training, and the Intel Early Access Program for software developers
www.intel.com/software/products	Programming tools to help you develop high-performance applications
www.intel.com/netcomms	Solutions and resources for networking and communications
www.intel.com/idf	Worldwide technical conference, the Intel Developer Forum

6176-0130-0482-7158

If serial number is missing, please send an
e-mail to Intel Press at intelpress@intel.com

IMPORTANT

You can access the companion Web site for this book on
the Internet at:

www.intel.com/intelpress/qpi

Use the serial number located in the upper portion of
this page to register your book and access additional
material, including the Digital Edition of the book.